Nature conservation and
the management of drainage channels

Chris Newbold, John Honnor and Karen Buckley

The authors wish to express their gratitude to the following members of the Nature Conservancy Council staff for their invaluable contributions to the text:

Dr B R Johnson for *Land drainage on the Somerset Levels*, in Chapter 1.

Dr M George for *Drained marshland in the Broads*, in Chapter 1.

M Palmer and B Banks for *Wildlife of ditches* in Chapter 3.

D K J Withrington for part of the Appendix on the legal aspects of the Wildlife and Countryside Act 1981 and the role of the NCC.

Contents

Foreword

We are pleased to introduce and welcome this important publication which we believe represents a significant step forward in the protection of Britain's aquatic wildlife. The opportunity now exists, alongside the vital need to protect urban and agricultural areas against flooding and to maintain existing land use, to provide a range of wildlife interests within the complex of mostly man-made watercourses.

The manual gives detailed guidance on the maintenance and care of lowland watercourses using methods which will conserve a rich plant and animal life. It aims to help create awareness amongst those who manage and control watercourses, drawing attention to the opportunities which exist, and advising on how their value can be sustained and enhanced. It represents the best knowledge and methods available today. Based on practical experience, it has been jointly prepared by the Association of Drainage Authorities and the Nature Conservancy Council to provide both an expert engineering and ecological input. It is an example of the determination of both organisations to continue to work closely together.

We are pleased to have played our part in stimulating this work and commend its application to all those whose job it is to manage lowland watercourses so that we can ensure that the environment in the future is at least as good as the one we enjoy today, and preferably, better.

David Riddington.

William Wilkinson,

Chairman
Association of Drainage Authorities

Chairman
Nature Conservancy Council

Introduction

Opportunities for wildlife

The aim of this management manual is to identify and encourage those practices which benefit and in many cases enhance wildlife within drainage channels and their banks, whilst achieving a standard of maintenance appropriate to the flood defence and land drainage needs of the area. Some of the ideas may mean changing channel profiles, some may require extra land, whereas others may require only a change in timing of work, a more stable water level or slight modification in operational practice.

This manual, published jointly by the Nature Conservancy Council and the Association of Drainage Authorities, is specifically aimed at lowland situations and is therefore of particular interest to drainage boards but also to the river authority in many areas of the country where interests extend into lowland catchments.

Its purpose is to provide guidance to those charged with maintaining the extensive and complex systems of lowland drainage works, to create awareness of opportunities and to give encouragement to grasp these wherever possible.

Land areas in blue are dependent upon complete systems for flood defence and land drainage.

There are in Great Britain approximately 11 million hectares of agricultural land, of which 5.5 million are dependent on some form of artificial drainage and can be termed 'lowlands' – see Figure 1. Of these, about two million hectares have been claimed from swamp and sea, and, without specific protection from tide and upland water and, often, pumped drainage also, they would not be habitable.

The distribution of the main areas of prehistoric wetland coincide with the lowland areas shown in Figure 1. It is no coincidence that present-day Sites of Special Scientific Interest (SSSIs) containing extensive ditch systems are situated in ancient wetland areas where drainage is still difficult. The most important of these grazing marsh sites are the Somerset Levels, Norfolk's Broadland, the Essex marshes, Pevensey Levels and Amberley Wild Brooks in Sussex, the North Kent Marshes, Sandwich Levels in Kent, the Derwent Ings in Yorkshire, Gwent Levels, the Vale of Trent and a few remaining fragments of Romney Marsh. Small remnants of fenland, intersected by ditches, still exist in some nature reserves, such as Woodwalton Fen in Cambridgeshire. Washlands, created to absorb winter floods, are often very important for their flora and fauna, examples being the Ouse and Nene Washes in Cambridgeshire.

The historical attempts to drain many of the ancient wetlands provide an insight into the difficulties faced by the drainage engineer. Three areas have been chosen to illustrate differences in approach to the drainage problem. These are the East Anglian fens, the Somerset Levels and Norfolk's Broadland.

The East Anglian fens

After the end of the last Ice Age some 10,000 years ago, the East Anglian fens would have been a raw, bleak, hummocky landscape with islands of gravel surrounded by clays and silt, all some 30-40 metres above sea level. As sea levels rose it became a wet, low-lying area dominated by fens, with wooded tracts of pines similar to the landscape of present-day Finland. The sea eventually flooded these forests, lapping at the foot of the chalk hills of southern Cambridgeshire, the Lincolnshire Wolds to the north and the Norfolk heaths in the east. The sea retreated gradually as the rivers created a vast delta. With thickening peat deposits the forests grew once again, but this time oak and beech predominated. Then the sea broke in again, drowning the trees and depositing a thin layer of clay. Once again the land became peat bog, the vast reed-beds hiding large meres. Trees grew on islands of higher ground. This was the landscape the Anglo-Saxons knew well and began to mould to their own needs. There is considerable evidence of Bronze Age and Roman occupation, but after the Roman withdrawal there was a further period of marine incursion and freshwater flooding from the uplands, so that when St Guthlac landed on the island of Crowland about 700 AD, as his biographer later wrote, "There is in the middle of Britain a hideous fen of huge bigness, which beginning at the River Granta [Cam] extends itself from the south to the north in a very long tract, even to the sea. Oft times clouded with moist dark vapours, no country man could endure to dwell in it by reason of such apparitions of devils were so frequently seen there." The Anglo-Saxons used the area to their best advantage, and by 1000 AD the settlements within or alongside the fens and marshes had become amongst the most prosperous in Britain. They had the benefit of virtually unlimited supplies of food – from the sea fish, shellfish, wildfowl and edible plants and from the freshwater marsh fish, eels, wildfowl and abundant forage.

Excellent farmland was gained by embanking and draining. The people were well fed and therefore healthy. Families were large and prosperous.

The Normans overlorded, co-ordinated and commercialised the agriculture, and trade with Europe expanded greatly. This demanded more land, and in the 150 years after the

Norman Conquest half the available fens and marshes, mostly on the silts and clays, were embanked and drained, mainly to provide sheep-grazing for the booming wool trade.

Economic decline from 1300 precluded further drainage, leaving uninhabited huge areas of mainly peat bog. Inundated each winter, they were nevertheless an important part of the economy, providing vast quantities of fish and fowl, thatch for roofing and peat for heating. In the 17th century the potential of the area for agriculture and the lack of formal ownership attracted the attention of speculators. The Earl of Bedford and thirteen 'Gentleman Adventurers' attempted to embank and drain nearly all the remaining wetlands. As the peat was drained, it shrank, thus creating more drainage difficulties; the horsemills powered by pack animals proved inadequate and wind-engines or windmills were deployed. These, however, tended to be 'gentle spectators' to the rising flood waters on calm days and it was not until the advent of steam drainage engines in the early 1800s that the fens could be said to be drained. Even so, many areas were still too wet to plough and only with the onset of the Second World War was the drainage of the whole area made adequate for arable crops.

Land drainage on the Somerset Levels

The first serious attempts to drain the great peaty basins of Somerset were made in medieval times by radically rerouting the rivers Brue and Axe. Sea walls and river embankments were raised and causeways were constructed to give access to the new lands. In some parts (Southlake for example), entire moors were walled off from the incessant flooding, allowing arable cropping of cereals and legumes. Other areas were cropped, some for their lush hay and others for alder firewood.

By 1600 some 22,000 acres (8,900 hectares) of the Somerset Moors, one third of the floodable land, had been converted to accessible and productive open grassland, but this was still inundated by annual winter flooding. A disastrous flood in 1607 prompted attempts to improve the drainage, but little changed until the advent of powerful pumps and enclosure by ditches in the 18th and 19th centuries.

Then the moors, previously used as common grazing, were divided by the now familiar patterns of narrow ditches, enclosing rectangular fields of about 5 to 10 acres (about two to four hectares). Fields were allotted to commoners in a way which led to the present-day complex system of fragmented land ownership. Field ditches became, as now, the responsibility of individual owners but the larger 'rhynes' were managed by Drainage Commissions, forerunners of today's Internal Drainage Boards (IDBs). A River Catchment Board was set up, responsible for pumping water from the moors into the main arterial drains, several of which were new cuts made between 1770 and 1850. By the mid 19th century the present day landscape of moist pastures and narrow drainage channels had been established. There was regular winter flooding, nowadays virtually absent over much of the Levels, and the meadows were still wet and inaccessible until early summer.

The Levels stayed like this, a remote refuge for wildlife, until the upsurge in agricultural improvement caused by the Second World War, when better flood alleviation and the introduction of artificial fertilisers and herbicides increased productivity of the pastures. In the drier conditions, farm machinery could enter the land in spring and many areas were converted from hay production to silage.

Before the War, most ditches were cleaned by hand using a hay knife to shear the vegetation and a crook to haul it on to the bank. This method is still used in a few areas. Nowadays most ditches are cleaned in autumn or winter by a tractor fitted with some form of ditching attachment. Ditching by machine is a skilled business, the operator aiming to remove the vegetation and a bare minimum of silt whilst still maintaining the ditch profile. Deep drainage with field under-drains is still relatively rare on the Levels. Most areas have high water levels, penned in summer to provide wet fences and drinking water for cattle. However, winter flooding has been much reduced in recent years, and spring water levels are generally low.

Drained marshland in the Broads

Far less is known about Broadland's drained marshland than about comparable areas elsewhere, for example the Fens. However, most of the land beside the relict estuary known as Breydon Water and the lowermost reaches of the rivers, consisted of saltings in the 13th century, and even today the meandering drainage channels characteristic of such terrain can still be made out, either in fossil form, or as part of the present-day drainage system. Nearer the margins of the valleys, the saltmarshes gave way to brackish and freshwater fen communities fed by run-off from the adjoining higher ground, whilst further up-river, where tidal influences and salinities were less, similar conditions extended right across the valley floor.

There were numerous sheep in the area at the time of Domesday, and the saltmarshes were probably used as sheep walks during the summer months, the animals being 'drifted' over the saltings and taken off when the latter were about to be flooded by a series of high spring tides – a similar form of management was practised on the north Norfolk saltmarshes until the outbreak of the Second World War. There is evidence that the sheep being grazed on the more accessible marshes were removed each evening and 'folded' on the higher ground nearby, thus improving its agricultural productivity.

There is documentary evidence that ditching and embankment works (fossatum), were being carried out during the late 13th and 14th centuries but the work of embanking the rivers and draining the adjoining marshland almost certainly extended over several centuries. In 1555, for example, some

"russhy" (sic) ground at East Somerton was dyked by Sir John Cleve after "it had long yielded him little profit by cause it lay opyn and onclosid." It is thought that the rivers were first embanked in their upper reaches since it would have been technically easier here than further downstream, where tidal influence was much greater.

Cattle as well as sheep were being kept on the marshes by the end of the 16th century. By analogy with the farming scene today, this may have reflected a change in farm economics, and in particular an increase in the relative profitability of raising cattle rather than sheep. But it is also possible that as sea, and therefore river, levels relative to the land rose, the frequent flooding to which the marshes would have been subject led to problems with liver fluke, whose most usual intermediate host, the dwarf marsh snail *Limnaea truncatula*, still occurs in the vicinity of Breydon Water.

Contemporary accounts indicate that, by the early 18th century, the drained marshland area was being managed in much the same way as it is today. Livestock, consisting mainly of cattle to be fattened but with smaller numbers of dairy cows, sheep and horses, would have been put out in the spring, the freeboard in the dykes being reduced to about half a metre so as to prevent them straying from one marsh to another. At the end of the grazing season, usually in early November, the dyke water levels would have been lowered to a metre or more below the marsh surface in order to provide as much storage capacity in the system as possible, and thus minimise the amount of flooding which took place in the winter and early spring.

Daniel Defoe (1722) greatly admired what he called the largest tract of meadowland in England and after a visit noted – "The gross of all the Scots cattle which come yearly to England are brought thither [to Broadland], being brought to [Horsham] St Faith where the Norfolk graziers go and buy them. These Scots 'runts' as they call them coming out of the cold and barren mountains of the Highlands of Scotland, feed so eagerly on the rich pasture of its marshes that they thus in an unusual manner grow monstrously fat, and the beef is so delicious for taste that the inhabitants prefer them to the English cattle which are much larger and fairer to look at."

Defoe was told that most of the 40,000 Scottish cattle arriving in Norfolk 'on the hoof' each year were fattened on the Broadland marshes. Allowing for the presence of some home bred beasts, this suggests that the stocking rate was not dissimilar to that customary today, if it is assumed that the process of reclamation had been largely, if not wholly, completed by the beginning of the 18th century.

Gravity drainage systems would have been used initially – and some marshland beside the upper reaches of the rivers in Broadland is still drained in this way – but windpumps, built of wood, are thought to have been introduced in the mid 17th century. The earliest-known brick towered structure is dated 1793. There were probably at least 200 windpumps in the region in the early 19th century, and some 20 were still in use in the 1930s. The last one worked until 1953.

Steam powered machinery is thought to have been introduced c1840, and some 30 such pumps were still in use in the 1930s. However, paraffin, and later, diesel-driven pumps superseded the steam-driven machinery from about 1915 onwards, and these in turn gave way to electric pumps from the late 1930s onwards.

Today's landscape in these lowland areas is of man-made channels, pumping stations and embanked rivers. Most of the land, including urban areas, is many metres below high-tide level and much is pumped. The extensive drainage and protection services are operated by IDBs and the National River Authority, without whose work vast areas would be uninhabitable.

Washlands

Historically, washlands were designed to hold excess winter flood water. The Ouse Washes in Cambridgeshire were designed by a 17th century Dutch engineer. Washes were created either in a low point in the catchment or in an area embanked alongside a major river. They prevented major flooding on valuable farmland and urban areas downstream. Occasionally, whole valleys were enclosed to prevent headwaters reaching lower, more vulnerable, parts of the catchment. West Sedgemoor in the Somerset Levels and Moors remains as an example of this unusual type of washland. As drainage efficiency increased, many washlands became redundant. This is particularly true of washlands in the now arable East Anglian fens of Cambridgeshire and Lincolnshire. Two notable washlands on the rivers Nene and Ouse still survive as an integral part of the modern-day drainage requirements for the Cambridgeshire fens. In spring these winter reservoirs have done their job of protecting the farmland beyond their embanked walls. Water is run off and the wet rushy meadows in these two washes are home to many rare as well as commonplace wetland breeding birds. The Ouse Washes in winter attract such large numbers of birds that they are of international importance for wintering wildfowl.

River engineers have begun, in the last decade or so, to consider the impact of a drainage scheme on the wildlife of the area and have embraced within their design, features which are more in sympathy with the environment. However, engineers should fully consider the effects of their actions on the hydrology, soil and water chemistry of fen, marsh and bog within the drainage area of a scheme. Some effects following drainage works are considered below — see also Chapter 9.

Hydrology and perched water tables

A 10 centimetre drop in the water table will markedly affect the living surface of a bog and the general lowering of water tables through drainage has affected many peatland areas but there are other more subtle and insidious effects on a wetland system.

Perched water tables

Calthorpe Broad National Nature Reserve in Norfolk lies in a peat basin where the hydrology is supported by a thin lens of clay. This clay layer extends beyond the reserve and was cut into by a scheme to deepen the drains in the fields beyond the reserve boundary. The water table in Calthorpe Broad is no longer perched but is connected with the levels in the drains outside the reserve. The previously stable water table in the Broad area fluctuates by approximately one metre in sequence with the level in the pumped and drained perimeter ditch.

Acid peats

The lowering of the water tables in Calthorpe Broad exposes the peat which dries out and becomes oxidised on exposure to the air. The ferrous cation is oxidised to a ferric cation to which an extra sulphate anion can be attached. When the water rises again, the iron in the peat is reduced back to a ferrous cation which releases a sulphate anion. Sulphates in water become sulphuric acid and the pH of Calthorpe Broad falls. Records of falls from the alkaline state of pH 7.5 to an acid state of pH 3.2 have markedly affected flora and fauna. Lily leaves have been scorched by the extreme acidity.

Similar releases of acid water into ditches on West Sedgemoor, Somerset have been caused by the deepening of drains within the moor. The chemistry of the peats is markedly different from Calthorpe Broad and involves sulphide zones in the peat being exposed by the new drains which leach out acid on contact with water.

Iron oxides

Many peat areas are rich in iron and the deepening of drains has resulted in iron oxides leaching out from the newly exposed peat. Tides of iron-rich water have swept into Horsey Mere in Norfolk from the nearby drainage channels, smothering and killing plant and animal life. Iron-rich deposits of peat are marked on soil survey maps so the problem could have been avoided.

Saline intrusion water

In many coastal areas freshwater overlies a saline water table because salt water has a greater density. If the freshwater table reaches a depth of 2 metres or more, a surface drain of 1.5 metres will only contain freshwater. Many drains around the coast of Norfolk developed a freshwater plant and animal community in response to this drainage pattern. During the 1960s and 1970s drains were deepened below the freshwater table and saltwater intruded into the new drains, killing all freshwater life.

Deflocculation of soils

Saline intrusion not only affects freshwater plants and animals but makes the ditch water unsuitable for irrigation needs. The salinity also affects soil structure. Sodium ions are capable of replacing the calcium ions in any clay lattice. If this happens the soil deflocculates, loses structure and becomes a clay solution. The roots of any arable crop are starved of oxygen and the plant dies. In some cases, after a land-drainage scheme the saline water is so close to the surface that many crops simply fail because the roots tap this zone and cannot tolerate the salinity.

Soil deflocculation can be remedied by treating the land with gypsum but it begs the question whether or not the land should have been drained in the first place.

Environmental assessment

All of the problems caused by breaking perched water tables – releasing acidity and iron oxides from peat, saline intrusion and soil deflocculation – could have been recognised and avoided had there been a survey of the land prior to a drainage scheme. During the 1960s and 1970s agricultural departments were asked to maximise agricultural production, and environmental considerations were often over-ridden by the desire to increase the total acreage of arable land. Future drainage schemes are unlikely to convert grassland to arable but engineers must be aware of the wider impact on wildlife which some improvements could cause. Any environmental assessment, required under statutory orders, must consider these wider implications.

For a naturalist, ditch-water in our grazing marshes is seldom dull. Even in the rich farmlands of East Anglia, a few ditches still hold echoes of the great waterlogged wilderness which once stretched from Cambridge and Peterborough to the Wash. The monk Felix, writing in the eighth century, described these vast marshes as "black waters o'erhung by mists, sometimes studded with wooded islands and traversed by the windings of tortuous streams." Charles Kingsley, lamenting the draining of Whittlesey Mere, recalled the glories of the Cambridgeshire fens in the first half of the 19th century in these words – "the coot clanked and the bittern boomed while high overhead hawk beyond hawk, buzzard beyond buzzard, hung motionless, kite beyond kite, as far as the eye could see. Far off upon the mere would rise a puff of smoke from a punt ... then down the wind came the boom of the great stanchion gun; and after that sound another sound, louder as it neared; a cry as of all the bells of Cambridge ...; and overhead rushed and whirled the skein of terrified wildfowl, screaming, piping, clacking, croaking, filling the air with the hoarse rattle of their wings, while clear above all sounded the odd whistle of the curlew and the trumpet note of the great wild swan."

The plants and animals harboured by many of our ditch systems represent the remnants of these ancient wetland communities. The extent to which the remnant resembles the original varies according to a number of factors, including continuity of habitat through time and modern-day management practice. Ditches in intensively farmed land are usually less interesting than those in the pasture land of grazing marshes, but nevertheless ditches may be the richest wildlife habitat in some arable landscapes.

The principal components of the wildlife of ditches, are water-plants, aquatic insects and other invertebrates, fish, amphibians and water-birds. The drier parts of the banks may perform much the same role as hedgerows, acting as wildlife corridors important for flowers, butterflies and bees, and providing nesting sites and cover for small birds and mammals. In arable farmland with few hedgerows, ditch margins may be the only remaining refuges for these terrestrial plants and animals. However, it is the aquatic community which is usually of most importance and some of the species are individually protected under the Wildlife and Countryside Act 1981. For a full list of protected animals and plants, see *Protecting Britain's Wildlife,* DoE, 1988.

Water plants

Aquatic plants are often classified according to their disposition in the water. Those growing beneath the surface, usually rooted in the bottom, are termed submerged. Examples are the milfoils and Canadian waterweed. Floating plants are of two types. Some, like the water-lilies, are rooted in the bottom but have leaves floating at the surface. Others, for instance the duckweeds and frogbit, float freely at the surface and have short roots dangling into the water. The third category, the emergent plants, have their roots submerged, but much of the leafy part of these plants grows well above the water. Examples are common reed, the reedmaces and water forget-me-not.

Some plants are difficult to pigeonhole into one of these categories. Yellow water-lily, for example, has large, translucent, submerged leaves as well as leathery, floating lily-pads, and some water-crowfoots have lobed, floating leaves as well as finely-divided submerged ones. Although a few submerged plants are water-pollinated, most have flowers which grow above the surface in order to take advantage of insect pollinators. Water-violet, for instance, is normally an inconspicuous plant with submerged fern-like leaves, but it becomes highly visible in the spring when whorls of flowers appear above the water, producing startling patches of lilac colour in some ditches. The water-soldier, which resembles the stiff, prickly crown of a pineapple, has the curious habit of floating to the surface at flowering time and sinking to the bottom in the autumn.

The most interesting ditches, from the point of view of a botanist, are those with a wide variety of the three types of water-plant. Ditches dominated by floating vegetation, such as duckweeds, can be poor in submerged species because little light penetrates through the floating mass, and sometimes oxygen is largely excluded from the water. There is a tendency in aquatic habitats for emergent plants progressively to invade the open water and compete with submerged vegetation. In the shallow water of ditches this process can be very rapid, and a fringe of common reed may spread across the whole of a narrow ditch in a year, if it is left unmanaged. Once this happens, the diversity of submerged species declines. In order to perpetuate a situation with a desirable mix of floating, submerged and emergent plants, regular management of the aquatic vegetation is necessary.

It is obvious that aquatic plants need water, but the depth of water required varies from species to species. Some plants are confined to a small depth range, whereas others are more generalist – see Table 1. Water-violet, for instance, needs shallow water less than half a metre deep, whereas lesser reedmace thrives best in water about 0.75 metre deep, but can grow from dry land out to two metres depth. The profile of a ditch is therefore an important factor influencing plant diversity. Shallower water species are most common in shallow ditches and the normal U shaped cross section of a deep drain prevents colonisation by such plants. Sometimes a relatively small drainage board may have a range of ditch sizes from the small and shallow to the large and deep. This too, is an important factor influencing plant diversity.

The 'ideal' ditch would have stands of tall, emergent plants such as common reed, reedmace and bulrush, but also shorter emergents such as bur-reed, water-plantain, sedges, water dock, water-cress, marsh-marigold, water forget-me-not, water mint and water-speedwells. Floating species might include moderate amounts of duckweed, but also larger plants such as broad-leaved pondweed, amphibious bistort, frogbit and yellow and white water-lilies. Common submerged plants of ditches are horned pondweed, spiked water milfoil, hornwort, curled pondweed, water-crowfoots and water-starworts. Numerous less common species occur in ditches.

There are approximately 170 species of freshwater and brackish water higher plants native to Great Britain. Higher plants include the flowering plants and ferns, but not mosses, liverworts or algae. Only about 40 of the aquatic higher plants do not occur in ditches, these being mainly species of stony upland lakes or fast flowing water. The richest ditches can contain more than 15 species of water plant per 20 metre length, but in intensive agricultural land whole ditches often have fewer than 10 species. A single drainage area may hold between 50-100 species and even occasionally over 100 species. Some species, such as frogbit, are seldom found elsewhere but in ditches. The national distribution of frogbit corresponds well with the distribution of the ancient southern wetland areas and therefore extensive ditch systems. Two rare aquatic plants, rootless duckweed and sharp-leaved pondweed, are also closely associated with ditches. The former is Britain's smallest flowering plant, hardly bigger than a grain of sand, which lives amongst rafts of other duckweeds. It occurs in ditches and peat cuttings on the Levels of Somerset, Gwent and Sussex. Sharp-leaved pondweed has been lost from a number of counties in Britain, and now survives almost exclusively in ditches, in a handful of places including Norfolk Broadland, Romney Marsh and Pevensey Levels.

Aquatic invertebrates

Ditches are equally important for aquatic invertebrate communities, especially snails, dragonflies, water beetles and some true flies, including soldier-flies, hover-flies and snail-killing flies. Freshwater snails are more abundant in the nutrient rich, calcareous waters of the lowlands than in upland lakes and rivers. For this reason, ditch systems harbour a great variety of these molluscs. Two nationally rare species, the shiny ram's horn and a valve snail *Valvata macrostoma,* are found in ditches in East Anglia, Kent and Sussex. Snails, being so much less mobile than insects, are slow to re-colonise cleaned ditches, and there is evidence from studies in Pevensey Levels that populations of these two rare species are particularly badly affected by large-scale dredging.

Ditches make ideal homes for many water beetles, which need a good cover of submergent vegetation and often damp, vegetated edges for hibernation. Over 50 of the 270 British species of water beetle can sometimes be found in a single ditch. The most spectacular of our water beetles is the great silver beetle which, at 5 centimetres in length, is Britain's second largest beetle, after the stag beetle. The great silver beetle is so called because of the gleaming bubbles which coat its underside, and which provide this aquatic insect with air. Its large, sluggish larva lives on snails, which it cuts open with powerful asymmetrical jaws. The national distribution of the great silver beetle shows the same kind of pattern as that of frogbit, and it, too, is highly dependant upon ditches for its survival. *Hydrochara caraboides* which is included in the British Red Data Books: 2 Insects, a smaller (up to two centimetres) relative of the great silver beetle, is even rarer and now occurs only in ditches and peat cuttings in a small area of the Somerset Levels, in places which were once acid bog.

The colourful dragonflies and damselflies are often the most obvious forms of insect life in and around ditches. Being predatory, they are dependent on the smaller, more inconspicuous invertebrates which live in and near the water. Like water beetles, dragonflies and damselflies need plenty of aquatic vegetation. Many species lay their eggs inside the tissues of submerged or floating plants, the female of some species actually crawling down the plant into the water in order to lay. The larvae of most species use the submerged parts of plants for cover, hiding amongst vegetation in order to avoid detection by predators and by their own prey. When the time comes to change into an adult, most dragonfly species use marginal plants as ladders and crawl up above the water in order to emerge from the larval skin. The newly-emerged adult clings to a stem or leaf while its wings expand and its body hardens, preparatory to its first flight.

The rarest of our dragonflies, the Norfolk aeshna, a large brown hawker, lives only in a few ditches in Norfolk Broadland. It is so rare that it has been granted special protection under Schedule 5 of the Wildlife and Countryside Act, 1981. The ditches in which the Norfolk aeshna breeds are well-vegetated and contain large growths of water-soldier.

Shallow water at the edges of ditches is essential for the air breathing larvae of some flies, such as hover-flies and soldier-flies. Snail-killing flies, whose larvae are parasitic on aquatic and amphibious snails, are also plentiful around the margins of ditches. Flowers on the banks and in adjacent meadows and drove ways, especially the large heads of cow parsley and hogweed, are important sources of food for nectar loving insects, especially hover-flies and soldier-flies. It is because ditches offer such a mosaic – deep open water, thick submergent vegetation, reedswamp, shallow margins, cattle-trampled mud, and flowery banks – that they can support such a wealth of invertebrate life.

Vertebrates

The most obvious fish of ditch systems is the pike, but sticklebacks and eels are very common. Tench, bream and rudd, which spawn on plants in slow-flowing waters with muddy beds, are all found in ditches and drains containing abundant aquatic vegetation.

Tadpoles are a familiar sight in some ditches, although they are rare in intensively farmed areas, for instance many areas of East Anglia. Where there is suitable terrestrial habitat, such as tall bankside vegetation, scrub and woodland, the commoner amphibian species can be abundant, as on the Offham Marshes and the Cuckmere Valley (East Sussex). Here common toads are particularly abundant, although there may also be substantial numbers of smooth newts, palmate newts and common frogs, the latter breeding mainly in shallow ditches or flooded fields. The great crested newt, whose tadpoles are very vulnerable to fish predation, only occasionally breed in ditches. In Kent and East Sussex the noisy presence of the introduced marsh frog is a feature of the marshes. This very aquatic species seldom moves far from the water, and does not therefore require areas of woodland or scrub.

Our rarest and most endangered amphibian, the natterjack toad, is protected under Schedule 5 of the Wildlife and Countryside Act, like the Norfolk aeshna and the great-crested newt. It occasionally breeds in very shallow ditches, particularly on the Duddon Estuary (Cumbria) where it breeds in shallow gutters which flow onto saltmarshes. By breeding later in the year it misses the high spring tides which kill the spawn of potential competitors, such as common frogs and toads. Unlike the other native species, this toad requires open, unshaded terrestrial habitat, preferably on a sandy substrate. Amphibians form a favourite food of the grass-snake, a reptile thoroughly at home in the water and seen occasionally in ditches draining grassland.

Two small aquatic mammals, the water shrew and the water vole, inhabit ditches. The water shrew is the more secretive and the scarcer of the two, occuring only in unpolluted ditches, and especially among water-cress. The harvest mouse is found occasionally in overgrown ditches, where it makes its nest in reed stems, often overhanging the water. Reed-beds were probably its original habitat, before cereal fields existed. Otters are rare in most of central and southern England, but some well-vegetated ditch systems, especially in Wales and south-west England, are important hunting grounds for otters, providing food in the form of sticklebacks and eels.

Well-vegetated ditches are important nesting sites for water birds such as coot and moorhen, mallard and shoveler ducks, water rail and little grebe. Stands of fringing reed are used as nesting sites by the reed bunting, sedge warbler and reed warbler. The rare Cetti's warbler nests in tangles of low, wet vegetation on ditch sides in southern England. The grey heron is a prominent feature of large, open ditches and drains as it waits for the passing fish or frog.

But the damp, tussocky meadows of grazing marshes and washlands are even more important for birds, as they attract breeding waders such as snipe, black-tailed godwit, curlew, lapwing and redshank. These populations suffer drastic declines when improved drainage enables the farmer to switch from hay to silage production. When the meadows come under the plough the losses are even greater. Snipe populations in England and Wales fell from around 10,000 breeding pairs in the late 1960s to under 2,000 pairs in 1982. Washlands and areas of grazing marsh which flood in winter attract huge flocks of wintering wildfowl, including Bewick's, whooper and mute swans, brent, pink-footed, graylag and bean geese, and ducks such as wigeon, pintail, teal, shoveler and mallard. Some of these areas are therefore of international importance for birds.

The range of ditch types

There are a number of types of ditch which are of particular importance for wildlife. Generally, ditches dominated by algae (blanket weed), very heavily managed watercourses, or ditches with widely-fluctuating water levels are poor in plant and animal life. A major cause of the decline of the common frog in East Anglia has been the drying-out of ditches in late spring and early summer. The typical grazing marsh wet fence, supporting floating plants, abundant submerged vegetation and a diversity of emergent species, provides a habitat for a range of animals. Ditches on peat have different assemblages of both plants and invertebrates compared with ditches on mineral soil. Wide drains usually have a different flora from the smaller watercourses, often being less dominated by duckweeds, but supporting broad-leaved pondweeds and the delicate shining pondweed, water lilies or arrowhead. The richest areas for ditch wildlife have a variety of ditches, ranging from the large and deep to the small and shallow, cut through peat and clays and having stable water levels.

Brackish ditches tend to be less diverse, but contain a number of scarce species not found in freshwater systems. Examples are brackish water-crowfoot, soft hornwort, and a number of rare water beetles. An area with a transition between brackish and fresh water is especially interesting, because a very wide variety of plants and invertebrates will be present. Such variety exists in the coastal marshes of North Kent in Romney Marsh and the Lewes Brook, East Sussex. An unusual feature of Romney Marsh is that the most saline ditches occur not near the coast but several miles inland, on badly drained peaty soil which has retained salt from some previous time when the marsh was covered by sea water.

Table 1   Depth and substrate tolerance of aquatic plants

Key: T – tolerates   P – prefers

Name	Peat	Clay	Silt	Depth (m)	Growth-form	Distribution/Comments
Arrowhead		P	P	0.1-0.5 (1.0)	Emergent	
Bistort, amphibious	T	P	P	Dry-3.0	Submerged	
Bladderwort, greater		P	P	0.1-2.0	Submerged	Widespread
intermediate	T	P	P	0.1-2.0	Submerged	Rare in drains
lesser	P			0.1-2.0	Submerged	More acid areas
Bogbean	P	T	T	Dry-2.0	Emergent/submerged	Forms rafts
Bulrush,	T	P	P	Dry-1.0	Emergent	Widespread, can be dominant
lesser		P	P	0.5-3.0	Emergent	Rare in drains
Bur-reed, branched		P	P	Dry-0.5 (1.0)	Emergent	Still water, can be dominant
least	P		T	0.5-3.0	Submerged	Rare in drains
unbranched	T	T	P	0.1-1.0	Emergent	Widespread, rivers
Club-rush, common	T	P	P	0.1-0.5 (1.0)	Emergent	Widespread
floating	P			0.1-0.5	Emergent	Mainly acid areas
grey		P	P	0.1-0.5 (1.0)	Emergent	More local in southern Britain
sea		P	P	0.1-0.5	Emergent	Coastal
Dock, water		P	T	Dry-0.1	Emergent	
Duckweed.	P	P	P	>0.1	Floating	Invasive, often dominant
rootless	T	P	P	0.5-3.0	Floating	Local
Frogbit	T	P	P	>0.1	Floating	
Hornwort, rigid	T	P	P	>0.5	Floating	Can grow uncontrolled
soft	T	P	P	>0.5	Floating	More coastal
Horsetail, water	P	P	P	(Dry)0.1-0.5(1.5)	Emergent	Forms dense beds
Mare's-tail		P		0.1-1.0	Emergent	Prefers calcium-rich waters
Marshwort, lesser	P			Dry-0.1-(0.5)	Creeping	More acid waters
Pondweed, blunt-leaved	T	P	P	0.5-4.0	Submerged	pH about 7.0±1
bog	P			0.1-2.0	Submerged	Rare in drains
broad-leaved	P	P	P	0.5-4.0	Submerged	Generalist, widespread
curled	T	P	P	0.5-3.0	Submerged	
fen	T	P	T	0.5-3.0	Submerged	Can be associated with shade
fennel	T	P	P	0.5-6.0	Submerged	Pollution tolerant
flat-stalked	T	T	P	0.5-2.0	Submerged	In silted drains
grass-wrack	T	P	P	0.5-3.0	Submerged	
hairlike	T	P	P	0.5-3.0	Submerged	Uncommon
horned		P	P	0.5-3.0	Submerged	Can be dominant
lesser	T	P	P	0.5-3.0	Submerged	Widespread in southern Britain
long-stalked	T	P	T	1.0-7.0	Submerged	In larger drains
opposite-leaved		P		0.5-2.0	Submerged	Prefers calcium-rich waters
perfoliate	T	P	P	0.5-4.0	Submerged	
red	P	T	T	0.5-4.0	Submerged	Mainly in peaty areas
sharp-leaved	P	T	T	0.5-2.0	Submerged	Nationally rare
shining	T	P	P	0.5-6.0	Submerged	
small	P	T	T	0.5-3.0	Submerged	Mainly in peaty areas
various leaved	P	T	T	0.5-3.0	Submerged	
Reed, common	P	P	P	Dry-0.5	Emergent	Forms floating rafts
Rush, bulbous	P			Dry-0.5	Emergent	More soft waters
flowering		P		(0.1)0.5-1.5	Emergent	Margins
Spike-rush, common	T	P	P	Dry-0.1	Emergent	Emergent at margins
slender	P			Dry-0.1	Emergent	More 'acid' margins
Sweet-grass, floating	T	P	T	Dry-0.5	Mats	Forms rafts rooted in shallow water
plicate	P	T	T	Dry-0.5	Mats	Forms rafts rooted in shallow water
reed	T	P	P	Dry-1.5	Emergent	Robust, invades margins
Water-cress,	T	P	P	0.1-2.0	Submerged	
fool's	T	P	P	(0.1)0.5-1.5	Mats	More calcium-rich waters
Water-crowfoot, brackish	T	P	P	0.1-3.0	Submerged	Brackish
common	T	P	P	0.1-3.0	Submerged	
fan-leaved		P	P	0.1-3.0	Submerged	
Ranunculus 'vertumnus'		P	T	0.1-3.0	Submerged	Larger drains?
R.peltatus		P	P	0.1-3.0	Submerged	
thread-leaved	T	T	T	0.1-3.0	Submerged	
Water-dropwort, fine-leaved		P	P	Dry-0.1(0.5)	Emergent	Margins
Water-lily, fringed	T	P	T	0.5-3.0	Submerged	Eastern England
white	P	T	T	0.5-3.0	Submerged	A 'marl' lake species
yellow	P	P	P	0.5-3.0	Submerged	Widespread and tolerant
Water-milfoil, alternate	P			0.5-6.0	Submerged	
spiked		P	P	0.5-6.0	Submerged	
Water-parsnip, lesser	T	P	T	(0.1)0.5-1.5	Mats	More calcium-rich waters
Water-plantain,	T	P	T	Dry-0.1(0.5)	Emergent	Widely distributed
narrow-leaved	T	P	T	Dry-0.1-(0.5)	Emergent	Southern Britain only
Water-soldier	P	P	P	0.5-1.5	Submerged	Invasive, often dominant
Water-speedwell, blue		P	P	Dry-0.5	Emergent	
pink		P	P	Dry-1.0	Submerged	Also riparian
Water-starworts, blunt-fruited		P		(0.1)0.5-1.5	Floating	
common	T	P	T	(0.1)0.5-1.5	Floating	
various-leaved		P		(0.1)0.5-1.5	Floating	
Water-violet	P	P	P	Dry-0.5	Emergent	Often forms dense beds
Waterweed, Canadian	P	P	P	0.2-4.0	Submerged	Invasive, can be dominant
Whorl-grass	T	P	P	Dry(0.1-1.5)	Emergent	Invades from margins
Yellow-cress, great		P	P	Dry-0.5	Emergent	

Types of drainage channel

Watercourses are designed, constructed and maintained to carry out various functions. Function often determines the size, shape, depth of water and intensity of maintenance. In assessing the possibilities for enhancing conservation interest it is essential to determine the drainage function and management requirements of any watercourse. Some of these are described as follows.

☐ The lowland valley river upstream of the coastal plain will often have flood meadows and/or flood storage reservoirs and may be navigable by small boats. The intensity of maintenance and the need for improvement depends upon a combination of the risk or hazards to the adjoining property and its value. Urban lengths must often need to be intensively maintained but in some cases there may be spare capacity allowing the introduction of conservation schemes. Watercourses in arable land need less vigorous management and those in pasture and flood meadows need only intermittent attention. There is great scope in the latter areas for extensive conservation work, examples of which are described later.

☐ The lower reaches of the lowland rivers carry the upland waters across the coastal plain to the sea. The water level is above the surrounding land and embankments, usually of earth, are constructed for flood protection. Maintenance here must be sufficient to prevent overtopping of the banks by floodwater. Submerged plants will require cutting or other forms of control at least once a year. Bank protection is vital, and scour and wave erosion must be prevented. Bushes and trees in flood embankments are not acceptable because tree roots dry out the earth, causing settlement and cracking. Woody vegetation also harbours burrowing animals which can destroy the water tightness and structure of banks. There are, however, a great many opportunities for grassland development with its associated flora and fauna. Banks can be grazed, cut and re-seeded with wild flowers, or left for nesting birds. These options are covered in more detail in Chapter 7.

☐ Internal drainage channels in both urban and arable land are often pumped and are usually within an Internal Drainage District. Land and property here is at its most vulnerable to flooding, and will lie behind river flood banks or sea defences, often below river and sea water levels.
Most rain falling within the drained area has to be evacuated via the man-made drainage channels and so the ability of these channels to convey water is vital to the existence and well-being of the community.

☐ Internal drainage channels in grassland areas drain these or grazing marshes sufficiently for good grass to grow. High water levels are retained for stock fencing and watering, and to prevent further land shrinkage in peaty areas. Conflicting requirements for water levels arise when attempts are made to mix arable and grassland farming.

Size and depth of drainage channels

Sub-surface field drains feed water into the private ditch, which in turn transports it into a larger drain, often controlled and managed by an Internal Drainage Board. These larger drains carry water into a main arterial drain, often via a pumping station, and thence out to sea. In many respects the drainage engineer has copied the natural drainage sequence of small streams, which coalesce and form a major tributary which in turn flows into a main river. All these have varying depths, depending on the volume of water to be transported from each part of the catchment. Drainage ditches are more regimented and they are more uniform in size and depth, but there are at least four arbitrary size and depth categories, corresponding to natural watercourses ranging from small stream to main river.

These four categories can be defined as follows –

☐ The small private ditch is up to 3 metres wide at the top and 1.5 metres deep. In arable areas such ditches often dry up in summer but in wet grassland they contain up to 1 metre depth of water.

☐ Many of the small private ditches in arable areas may have been filled in to create larger fields and the capacity of those remaining has been increased. Where they serve a number of occupiers they become IDB watercourses. These are up to 8 metres wide and 3 metres deep with a carefully controlled water level in summer and winter to suit the local need. They can be fully reached by a hydraulic excavator but will not float a boat.

☐ The intermediate IDB channel has a waterway over 10 metres wide and 3 metres deep and will take boat-mounted equipment. Water levels are carefully controlled by a pumping station and sluices.

☐ Ditches in the final category can be more than 20 metres wide and 5 metres deep and receive waters from many catchments and pumping stations. They may be embanked as carrier drains, transporting upland water across the coastal plain to the sea, and come under IDB or National River Authority jurisdiction.

In any drainage area there is a definite stepwise progression in size and depth, but over the country as a whole there is a continuum from the small to the large. Each size category is dug to carry a calculated volume of water from each segment of the drainage area.

Drainage standards – management practice and their impact on wildlife

Drainage channel management varies throughout the country but some of the factors which influence management are the drainage standards necessary to ensure protection from flooding, the soil type and farming practice. Where drainage standards are seen as a priority concern the ditches and banks are often intensively managed. Wildlife interests are often not considered and yet small changes in management could bring some advantages to wildlife.

The intensity of maintenance depends on the flood risk or hazard to the surrounding land which results from not carrying out that maintenance. For catchments containing urban areas, channels must be kept as clear as is necessary for them to carry away flood waters, which means cutting may be required two or three times per season. For arable areas, the bottom is cleansed and the banks are cut often twice per season where bed gradients are flatter than 1 in 1,000, and once where the slope is steeper.

In many ditches in clay the drain profile tends to be very stable and may have to be reshaped only every 7-15 years. Water tables are kept normally at least one metre below land level. Dry ditches and larger banksides are either cut or flailed once to three times a year. In the Gwent Levels in South Wales a mainly grassland area on clay, the large and intermediate drains are cut and cleansed every 1–3 years and re-dredged where necessary every seventh year. Smaller, often private, ditches are dredged on a need basis every 10-50 years but they will be cut every 1–3 years.

Peat, alluvium and sand is generally less stable so slumping can be a problem. Annual or more frequent cutting is commonplace but engineers are usually careful to cut above the bottom, as scraping can lift the vegetation mat which protects and binds the soil below water level.

Where all these soils are under arable or grass leys the needs of agricultural productivity determines that drainage requirements take priority. Spare drainage capacity wastes valuable agricultural land so many ditches are of a size to accommodate the designed flow with no spare capacity. The fear of that occasional flood means that ditches are kept rigorously cleansed.

In most ditches water levels may be kept lower in winter where drainage is seen as a priority, but in summer can be raised for irrigation, wildlife and amenity purposes.

Wildlife can and often does survive even in the most intensively managed areas but it can be very patchy. There are the occasional remainder drains left as wildlife areas. These are drains which have been replaced in a rationalisation of the drainage pattern. In some, particularly the larger drains in arable areas, bankside and fringe vegetation has less effect on the flow capacity and so cutting and clearing can be less rigorous on the margins.

Drainage standards – the grazing marsh and its management

The traditional grazing marsh has declined markedly in the last 40 years. River engineering schemes and drainage grants have given farmers the opportunity and incentive to drain these valuable wildlife areas. Prior to such schemes, some farmers have tried to grow arable crops by raising banks around their fields or have cultivated slightly higher ground on the edge of the grazing marsh and have thus been able to avoid most annual floods.

In Romney Marsh, the River Rother was enlarged between 1967 and 1972 and gave security within the marsh from the annual flood. A change to arable was inevitable here, and in other areas where rivers have been enlarged. Similarly, areas in Norfolk's Broadland have seen dramatic changes in land-use from grazing marsh to arable.

It is in the remaining grazing marsh ditches of England and Wales that the need for management is comparatively less rigorous. High water tables throughout the year with an occasional or annual winter flood are indicative of the poor drainage of the area. The potential for increased agricultural production is there but economics have dictated that these areas remain poorly drained.Because of intractable soils or a host of engineering reasons, these are truly the last relicts of the ancient wetlands.

In many grazing marshes, farming has adapted to the limitations imposed by poor drainage standards. Summer grazing, the hay crop or the occasional silage crop depend on the timing and extent of the winter and spring flood. Many farmers accept this and have been content to carry on traditional farming practices. Ditch management on such land is often in sympathy with nature conservation although many ditches are often de-watered in winter which must adversely affect this aquatic wildlife. Even so the farmers and IDBs have maintained an aquatic interest through regular light cleansing and light management. Many peat ditches in the Somerset Levels and Moors are cut and profiled by hand annually and, as elsewhere, act as wet fences to contain stock. Some overgrown ditches are re-profiled with a bucket mounted on a tractor – this is a relatively inefficient method when compared with more modern machinery. Cattle may poach and trample the sides, producing a varied profile in the ditch. It is little wonder that the traditional grazing marsh ditch contains rich pockets of wildlife. Such interest is not confined to the ditch and its bankside. These can be bordered by herb-rich hay meadow or edge ancient drove ways where the wide verges abound with flowers and butterflies. Nor is the interest confined to one season – the winter floods host a myriad of wildfowl.

Sympathetic management and the drainage ditch

Land-use change since 1945 stresses the need to conserve, through sympathetic management, the remaining grazing marsh. The Drainage Authorities have a duty to consider the needs of wildlife, so far as it is consistent with their everyday drainage activity, in all areas, as well as grazing marsh. Drain profiles can be modified to give more physical diversity to the drainage channel and increase the aquatic interest. Low-growing 'low maintenance' seed mixtures can be sown on the banks, thus opening up the sward and allowing an attractive flora to grow from dormant seeds. Habitat reinstatement will increase the wildlife interest in any intensively managed drainage area. Many examples are considered in detail in the Management sections – see Chapters 5, 6 and 7. Even small sympathetic changes in management techniques and engineering practices can greatly enhance animal and plant life. The general principle of channel management which sustain wildlife interest are considered in the next chapter.

Introduction

The previous chapter has discussed the range of channel sizes and their management. In Sites of Special Scientific Interest the NCC will recommend the practices outlined below as part of the statutory consultation with IDBs and farmers. See Appendix. An IDB can also increase the wildlife interest in any ditch by following five essential management principles.

These are –

☐ The range of aquatic wildlife is dependent upon the depth of water held in the drainage channel.

☐ Most aquatic wildlife is dependent on a stable water level over any year.

☐ The quality of water is crucial to both wildlife and drainage. Poor water quality results in algal blooms, duckweed and cott which have few friends.

☐ Conservation management within the channel and on the banks is essential.

☐ Habitat creation, re-instatement or restoration can provide more varied habitats for wildlife, increasing the number of species in or along any drainage channel.

Size and depth and the wildlife interest

The different depths and sizes provide a range of habitats for wildlife – see also Chapter 3. Some plants are adapted to a narrow depth range. Other more generalist species are adapted to a range of water depths – see Table 1. In deeper drains assuming they are full of water the steep sides of the 'U' or 'V' shaped profile prevent colonisation by shallow-water species. Over any catchment or drainage area, 50–100 species of truly aquatic and semi aquatic plants could be found in the different channel sizes.

However, individual ditches may contain less than 10 species. There are many ways by which this number can be increased without forfeiting the drainage channel's original purpose.

Deeper channels can be reprofiled and a shallow shelf or berm created along selected lengths. Shallow channels can have deeper ponds dug into a junction at a field corner. An increase in the number of plant species usually results in an overall increase in the diversity of animal life. For more ideas see the Management sections in Chapters 6 and 7. Clearly a stable water level is essential if the varying depths created within the channel are to succeed as wildlife habitats.

Stability of water levels and wildlife interest

Many reservoirs have a bare drawdown zone where very few species survive. Similarly, fluctuating water levels in ditches restrict the number of species at the water margin. The effects may be even worse for aquatic wildlife. In a reservoir, a body of water remains. Some ditches can be dry in summer but wet in winter and spring. Others may be purposely de-watered in winter and re-watered in summer. The drying out in late spring/summer of East Anglian ditches was a major cause of the decline of the common frog in most of them. Stable water levels are an essential feature of many of the most interesting ditches.

Water quality and wildlife interest

For different reasons, neither the engineer nor the conservationist likes a blanket cover of algae, duckweed or a matted tangle of cott *Vaucheria* sp. at the bottom of the ditch. There are two primary causes of this type of problem. The first cause and perhaps the most important is enrichment from the surrounding farmland due to fertiliser run-off, silage liquor and animal slurries and effluent from town and village sewage treatment works; the second cause is too-frequent maintenance of the ditch which eliminates the submerged higher plants and emergent plants. There is a fundamental relationship between a higher plant community and algae. Higher plants can partially control algae through competition factors and animals can partially control algae through grazing. The two together can effectively control algae. Eliminate or suppress this community and the algae take over.

Conservation management of channels and ditches

Without regular maintenance, ditches become overgrown and silt up, losing much of their plant and animal interest. Sympathetic forms of management are thus an essential part of conservation. Traditional methods adopt a 'little and often' approach, relying on handcutting with scythes, peat spades or sharp chains. The latter are dragged across the ditch bottom by two men, one on either side of the ditch. With care, modern machinery can emulate these forms of management. When ditches have been left for longer periods of time, they require more radical forms of management. A bucket on the back of a tractor removes tall emergent plants, coarse grasses and scrub, creating open water. The advantage to conservation lies in the inefficiency of this practice; patches of vegetation are left and the bottom is irregular. Modern machinery is not so inefficient but could be made so, in most instances, in the hands of a skilled operator. With any form of regular maintenance there is a rapid change in vegetation followed by a period of recovery.

The long term effect of sympathetic regular maintenance may be to keep the ditch at one fixed stage of development. Although a large proportion of the annual production is removed, an almost identical vegetation often develops over the ensuing months from the fragments of vegetation and seed left behind. Where the ditch is maintained sympathetically on a 'little and often' basis, the differences in vegetation from one year to the next may be minimal. The differences are more striking where the ditch is maintained less frequently and becomes overgrown. Recently cleansed ditches represent the open water stage and support a diverse plant and animal life. Those about to be cleansed represent a linear reedswamp. If the radical cleansing of ditches is carried out on a rotational basis, say one third to one fifth every two years over a period of 6–10 years, the drainage catchment can include examples of the different plant and animal communities contained in open water, progressing through to a linear reedswamp. Such radical forms of management are possible on sections of remainder channels. Clearly, also, a range of drain widths and depths adds to the physical diversity and enlarges the range of possibilities for different plant and animal communities.

Embankments are cut annually in June as a hay crop, or in the autumn. Sometimes the management is less frequent, with cutting only every three years. Some banks are allowed to scrub over before being 'brushed' to contain growth. Some banks may contain a mix of these management ideas to give maximum species diversity.

Ditches within washlands such as the Nene and Ouse Washes are managed either on a 'little and often' basis or they are more radically reprofiled as and when necessary. In washlands, the local drainage need is lower and a corresponding reduction in the drainage standard is possible. Water levels are the most important factor in washland management. If the winter level is too deep, dabbling duck and other wildfowl cannot feed on the seeds scattered in the submerged wet meadow. If the water is retained well into the spring, potential breeding birds seeking the wet meadow are put off. The balance between winter and spring levels is critical – see Chapter 9. As an illustration of the importance of these management principles – the depth and quality of water, the stability of water levels and the conservation management of drainage channels – the attributes of some SSSIs are discussed. Many ditches of Sites of

Special Scientific Interest (SSSIs) quality have a stable and relatively high water table. Most are found in the grazing marshes of Britain; some are found in relict fenland which is now intensively farmed. One such drain, Cross Drain, in the Welland and Deeping IDB, Lincolnshire, has been cut through acid peat and has a base layer of gravel. In one sense it is a headwater drain, the water from other drains being fed to other parts of the drainage catchment. It has a stable water depth of at least one metre, the peat gives a slightly acid water and the gravels are a source of pure alkaline water. It is the purity and slight acidity of the water which has helped maintain its remarkably diverse relict invertebrate fauna. The gravel base prevents undercutting of the root mat during annual maintenence works so plant re-growth is rapid. The invertebrate community contains 54 species of beetle, including two nationally rare species and several other notable species. The plant community contains two nationally scarce species and several species uncommon in Lincolnshire.

Certainly, areas such as Cross Drain cannot survive without the maintenance carried out by an IDB, but the wildlife there is also dependent on the special physical attributes of the peat and gravel substrates and a source of 'pure' groundwater.

Other areas, such as parts of the Somerset Levels and Moors, contain semi-improved grazing marsh. Here the most interesting ditches are often headwater drains. These are unaffected by those accumulative enrichment problems further down the catchment, which are associated with intensive farming. At Amberley Wild Brooks, in Sussex, spring water from underlying Greensand purifies and dilutes minor effects of saline intrusion water from the tidal River Arun.

This chapter reviews the many channel management options open to an IDB and include the management principles previously outlined in Chapter 5.

Many options emphasise a more appropriate approach to management; others give opportunities for habitat re-instatement.

Channels from the engineering viewpoint must be cleared of vegetation at frequent intervals and re-dredged to maintain the profile by various types of machine.

They are kept clean of vegetation and reprofiled for many reasons, but the following are the most important to prevent flooding –

☐ The drainage channel profile has been designed to transfer a specific flow, thereby avoiding flooding. Vegetation impedes flow by increasing the rugosity or friction of the channel.

☐ Frequent cleansing of the channel bed gives longer periods between de-silting.

☐ Channels are reprofiled to maintain an efficient flow.

☐ Channels have very little spare capacity to hold excess water, being designed to accommodate excessive run-off during a summer storm or high water flows in winter to a given freeboard.

Rigorous maintenance has often produced ditches in which only the most tolerant and resistant species survive.

A more sympathetic approach, which creates greater opportunities for wildlife within the drainage channel whilst still maintaining their primary function of land drainage, is considered in this chapter.

Management planning

Most of the management ideas require some form of planning. Cutting schedules will have to be identified which suit the wildlife needs. It is possible that day-to-day maintenance operations on chosen lengths should be re-scheduled to be carried out later in the year.

Option 1

Selective removal of waterplants to permit recolonisation 1

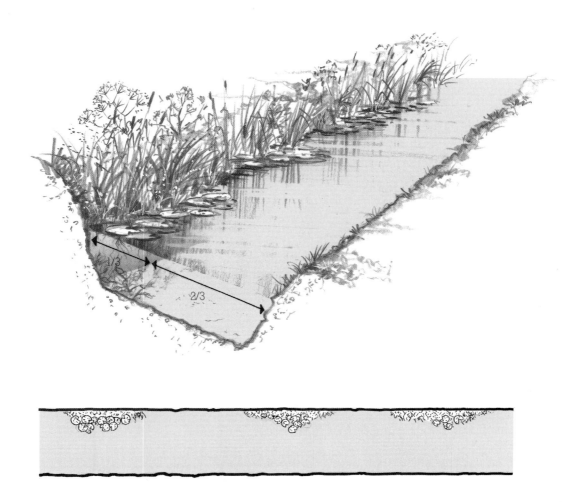

Size of watercourse >2 metres

Description In a dredging operation, leave a continuous strip of emergent and aquatic plants.

Purpose To foster wildlife. There is no direct land-drainage advantage.

Method Dredge two thirds of the width of the channel, leaving one third of the width untouched.

Conservation advantages Continuity of the plant community permits the establishment of an associated invertebrate and vertebrate animal community including, for example, dragonflies and fish. It also permits the development of a varied plant structure which encourages a wider range of wildlife.

Option 2

Selective removal of waterplants to permit recolonisation 2

Size of watercourse >1 metre

Description In a dredging operation leave patches of wetland plants.

Purpose To foster wildlife. There are no direct land-drainage benefits except where plants protect the toe of the bank from erosion.

Method Dredging a continuous but sinuous route leaving plants in patches on alternate sides.

Conservation advantages This option retains emergent and aquatic species but it also increases diversity in the structure and mix of species. This is because of the changes in velocity on meanders, particularly where the fringes are dominated by near-monocultures of reed sweet-grass and reed canary-grass. There are also benefits to invertebrates and fish.

Option 3

Selective removal of waterplants to permit recolonisation 3

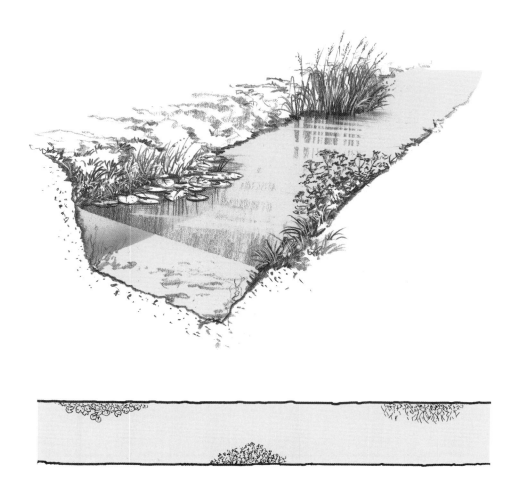

Size of watercourse All

Description Leaving patches of wetland plants.

Purpose To foster wildlife. There are no direct land-drainage advantages.

Method Select specific, easily identifiable, species for retention but periodically reduce the size of the area covered, for example yellow waterlily. Consult your local wildlife trust for advice.

Conservation advantages The deliberate retention of species which are thought aesthetically pleasing by the public will also add structure and diversity to the habitat and increase the wildlife interest.

Option 4

Selective removal of waterplants to permit recolonisation 4

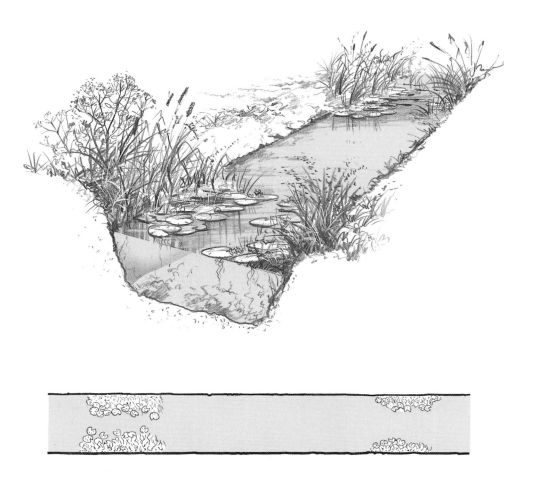

Size of watercourse All

Description Leaving patches of emergent and aquatic plants.

Purpose To permit recolonisation during the period of the dredging programme. There are no immediate land-drainage benefits, nor would this option be suitable for every part of a watercourse.

Method Selectively dredge a watercourse to leave plants in blocks of 10 metres every 30 metres.

Conservation advantages This option makes the retention of the diversity of the plant community and its associated fauna easier. No specialised knowledge is needed if the community is uniform. Plants and animals can recolonise the dredged sections which can be overdeepened to form pools.

Channel

Option 5

Selective removal of waterplants to permit recolonisation 5 – capital schemes, involving major reprofiling of channel

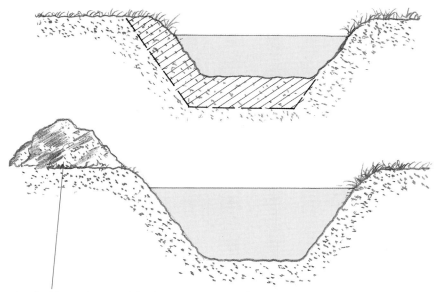

Spoil either to be used for the construction of a new bank or to be spread across the field.

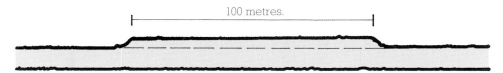

100 metres.

Re-profiling the ditch on one side for alternative lengths of about 100 metres.

Size of watercourse All

Description Leaving lengths of emergent and aquatic plants for removal in future years.

Purpose Permits the recolonisation by plants and animals from the undredged to the dredged section. There are no immediate land-drainage advantages.

Method When reprofiling or deepening a channel, work on one side only. Work say, 100 metre blocks, leaving intermediate blocks of the same length untouched. When worked stretches have recolonised satisfactorily (as advised by naturalists), reprofile the remaining sections. To increase the chances of recolonisation plant out newly worked stretches with a selection of plants removed during reprofiling.

Conservation advantages The enlarged channel will be recolonised by species from nearby untouched sections. Recolonisation will be more rapid and more nearly duplicate original communities.

Option 6

Scalloping vegetation to create meanders

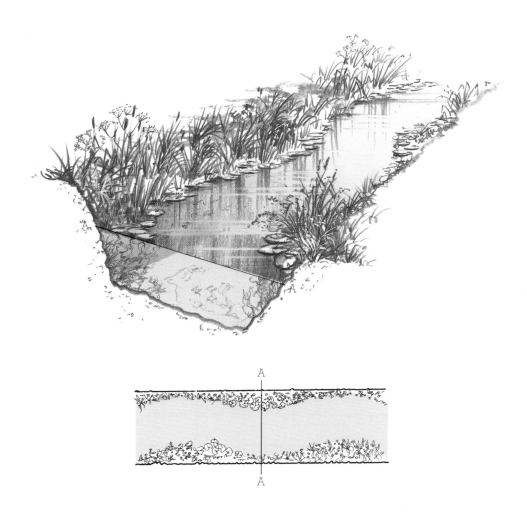

Size of watercourse >2 metres

Description Leaving patches of wetland plants on alternate sides.

Purpose To foster wildlife. There is no particular land-drainage advantage. However, it does serve to slow down the speed of water flow in normal conditions, but in flood conditions the water will still flow in a straight line.

Method Remove silt and plants on alternate sides to create a sinuous channel for the water flow. Such meanders often develop naturally within enlarged channels and these can be accentuated.

Conservation advantages Creates diversity of structure in the channel which benefits both plants and invertebrates.

Option 7

Re-introduction/re-distribution of plants

Size of watercourse All but the deepest.

Description To re-introduce plants or re-distribute plants along and within a drainage channel.

Purpose There is no land-drainage advantage. Benefits will be mainly for wildlife. Aquatic plants may also compete with less desirable species such as algae and help as a biological control agent.

Method Following consultation with wildlife experts, re-plant into short stretches of channel attractive or beneficial plants from similar sites nearby or from elsewhere in the system. These can then colonise and spread. This is particularly feasible where the flow is minimal, the channel large and dominated by undesirable species such as algae.

Conservation advantages Plant diversity is increased and this promotes a greater diversity of animals. Where no plant propagules remain within the system, re-introduction is the only available option.

Channel

Option 8

Creation of pools

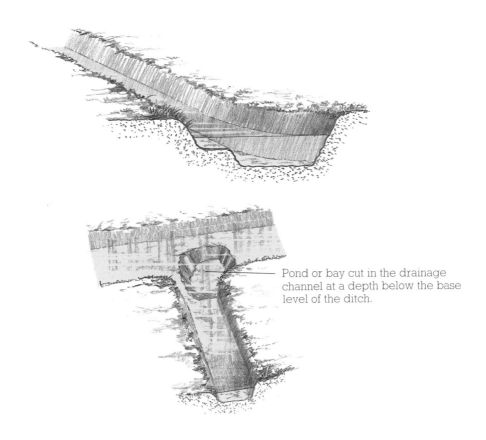

Pond or bay cut in the drainage channel at a depth below the base level of the ditch.

Size of watercourse >2 metres

Description An overdeepening of the channel bed to form a pond at the junction of minor ditches. Land take may be necessary and care exercised to retain bank stability.

Purpose To provide permanent and deeper water on smaller watercourses, many of which have a reduced flow or dry out in summer.

Method The profile of the pool is important. Where space permits, this should be stepped with the deepest water in the centre. Overhanging trees should not be part of this feature as they will cause natural enrichment of the static water and reduce the abundance of invertebrates by shading the pond. The spoil may be used for increasing the height of the banks or spread on adjacent land. This may be a suitable task for conservation volunteers.

Conservation advantages Creates a refuge for amphibians, invertebrates and possibly fish where there is little residual summer water flow. Many wetland plants and animals cannot adjust to periodically dry conditions. The pools will provide a continuity of habitat for wetland plants and animals.

Option 9

Reed-bed purification treatment

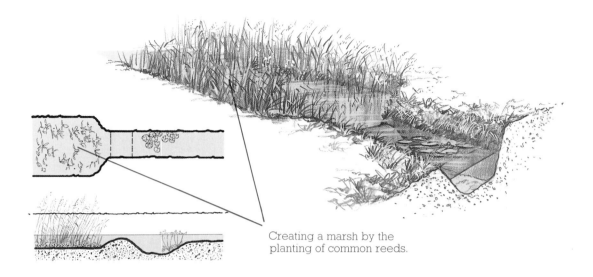

Creating a marsh by the
planting of common reeds.

Size of watercourse Most applicable to small ditches draining farmsteads, where accidental enrichment may occur. The larger the watercourse, the greater the potential land-take.

Description A dense planting of common reed *Phragmites australis*, through which the water flow is directed, forming a marsh. The size and shape of the reed-bed would be dictated by the volume of water and the level of enrichment that could occur.

Purpose To act as a fail safe mechanism where there is the possibility of enrichment from organic material. A reed-bed can help remove excess nutrients such as nitrates and to some extent phosphates and bring benefit elsewhere by helping to reduce algal growth lower down the system. However it should not be looked upon as the solution to cleaning water to a standard acceptable to the River Authority under the Control of Pollution Act 1974.

Method Widen the existing watercourse to form a long flat basin approximately 0.25 metre below the existing bed level and covering the area of the desired reed-bed. Plant either with scoops of material from existing reed-beds which are being dredged for other reasons or purchase plants from centres specialising in producing reed for the water industry. A very shady site is not desirable as shade will depress reed growth. If desired the lower end of the excavated section can be deepened to produce open water. For further advice on planting a reed-bed see Option 22.

Conservation advantages Removal of those excess nutrients which favour algal growth. These compete with and often exclude desirable plants. A habitat is created which can be used by specialist birds such as reed bunting and reed warbler. The introduction of marsh plants such as purple-loosestrife, meadow-rue, lady's smock and marsh-marigold will be both beneficial to invertebrates and aesthetically very pleasing.

Option 10

Silt-traps

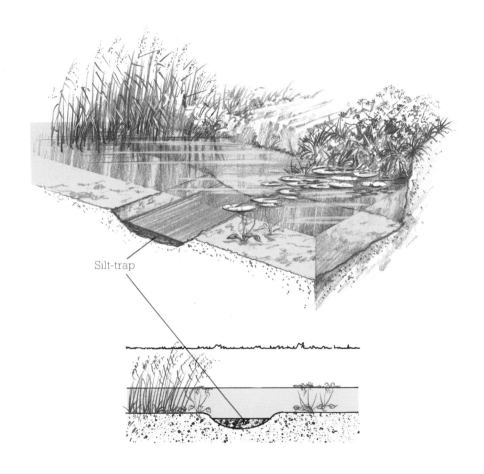

Silt-trap

Size of watercourse >2 metres

Description Sites where silt can be encouraged to settle out and be selectively dredged. This may be an essential condition if new roads are constructed across major or minor drains since oils and other pollutants can be caught in a properly designed silt-trap.

Purpose To obviate the necessity for regular desilting operations over long lengths of channel. Pollution problems may be contained within the silt-trap.

Method Selection of sites need to be easily accessible to machinery on a regular basis. Sites should also show a natural accumulation of silt or a pool feature where silt can be encouraged to settle out. Such sites are often associated with bridges. A silt-trap can be associated with the sluice option – see Option 14.

Conservation advantages Desilting operations and pollutants are potentially confined to small lengths of the drainage channel allowing the remainder of the watercourse to develop a stable plant and animal community.

Channel

Option 11

Leaving headwaters untouched

Size of watercourse >2 metres

Description Reducing the frequency of dredging and cutting on channels in the headwaters of watercourses and at the beginning of drains where flooding is not a consideration.

Purpose A reduction in management costs is possible. The drain is managed at a low level for the benefit of wildlife and without disbenefit to adjacent land-use.

Method Identify sites with the agreement of the landowners. The channel could be left to develop a linear marshland perhaps with overdeepened areas forming ponds. The banks could be managed in a variety of ways. A mosaic of scrub cut every three years and annually-cut grass would give the greatest diversity – see the bank management options. Long term management may be necessary, such as selective cutting to control the invasion of marshland by scrub, and the restoration of sites that have dried out.

Conservation advantages Relatively undisturbed linear marshland sites could develop with corresponding benefits to breeding birds, amphibians, reptiles, invertebrates and plants.

Channel

Option 12

Stabilising of bed at culvert mouths

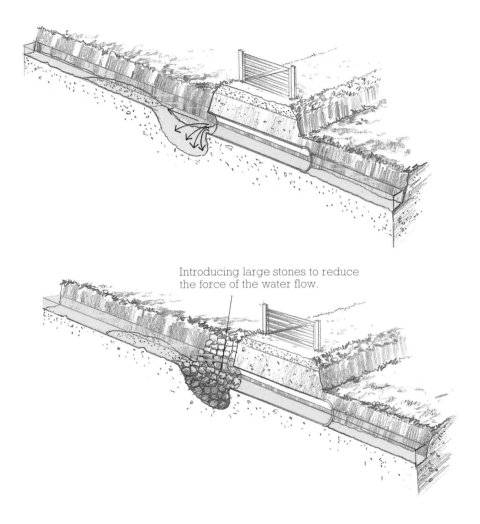

Introducing large stones to reduce the force of the water flow.

Size of watercourse All under 1 metre deep.

Description To stabilise the water flow at the mouth of culverts.

Purpose Reduces the erosive force of waterflows which are of a higher velocity at the mouth of culverts.

Method Introduction of large stones into the channel immediately where the water leaves the culvert.

Conservation advantages These sites often develop good vertical banks and pools. Stabilising the exit should protect these features which would be removed by the use of gabions or concrete mattresses.

Option 13

Low level by-pass channels

Three options for managing a by-pass channel.

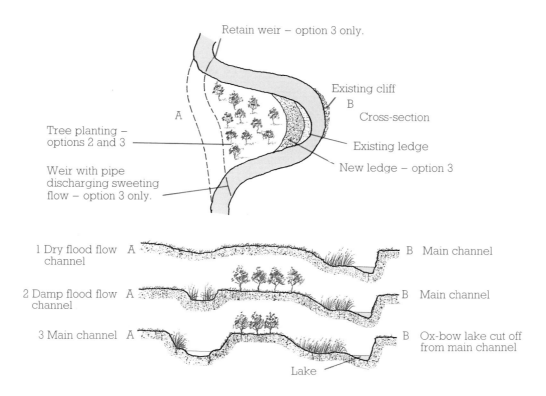

Size of watercourse Relates to the meandering channels typical of natural watercourses.

Description An alternative channel bed at a similar level to the main channel, which carries water during increased flows giving the main channel a 'braided' appearance.

Purpose A method of obtaining extra flow capacity as soon as there is an increase in water level, helping to prevent problems with flash floods. However, this option is likely to result in additional land-take.

Method The by-pass channel may be; a former meander loop cut off by a capital works programme; a route kept open behind a gravel shoal, which itself may be covered in flood conditions or a purposely dug channel across a meander loop. All should retain some water during low, main channel flows, so that a wetland community can develop. Where desirable, the by-pass channel may be controlled by a weir.

Conservation advantages This option permits the development of wetland communities in the by-pass channel and retains natural features such as meander loops, shingle shoals and vertical banks within the main channel without affecting the land-drainage function of the watercourse. For this option to benefit fish breeding and wildlife generally, the by-pass channels should not be dry.

Option 14

Sluices

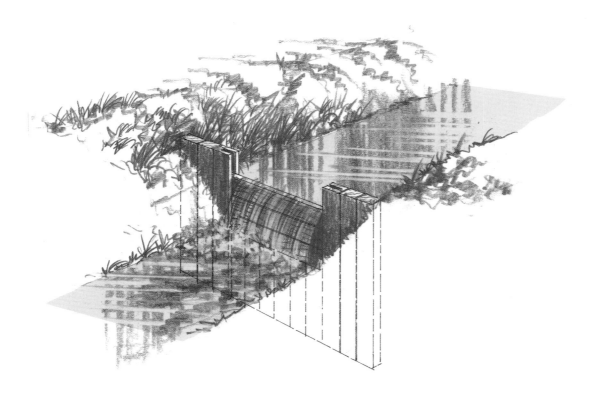

Size of watercourse All

Description Regulation of water levels.

Purpose To foster ditch wildlife andor maintain wet meadows for wetland birds. Sluices will also keep the water table high during peak crop growth, or act as wet fences for stock in grazing marsh systems. They can also store water for irrigation needs but drawdown could affect the wildlife interest.

Method Structures can be made from wood or concrete. They can be permanent or have movable boards to permit water to run away faster in flood conditions. They can provide sensitive water level controls in nature reserves using movable boards in multiples of 150 millimetres.

Conservation advantages Maintenance of high water tables or the maintenance of variable water tables on a field-by-field basis. High water tables will benefit fen and marsh. They could provide wet feeding areas in adjacent meadows for wetland birds. Aquatic plant and animal communities will benefit from a high and more stable water table.

Option 15

Borrow pits

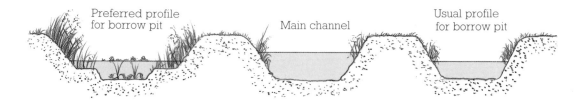

Preferred profile for borrow pit

Main channel

Usual profile for borrow pit

Size of watercourse Only relevant to channels with flood banks or sea defence banks.

Description Pits excavated to provide spoil.

Purpose To create, restore or enlarge flood banks and provide a habitat for wildlife.

Method Many pits already exist and may require management or improvement for nature conservation. Others could be created. Historically, borrow pits have been deep oblong holes with vertical sides. It is preferable that the profile should be irregular with some banks containing berms or, alternatively, angled into the water thereby encouraging a greater diversity of plants.

Conservation advantages The most interesting borrow pits have shallow sloping banks where plants can gain a foothold and light can penetrate to the bottom. Some constructed in the last century are now Sites of Special Scientific Interest. Many are stocked and used by fishing clubs.

Conservation disadvantages Sea defence works could take spoil from a saltmarsh which would undoubtedly be of higher conservation value than the newly created borrow pit. The creation of an artificial borrow pit cannot replace the loss of semi-natural habitats such as saltmarsh, which is a threatened and diminishing habitat.

Off-Channel

Option 16

Gull or blow hole pond

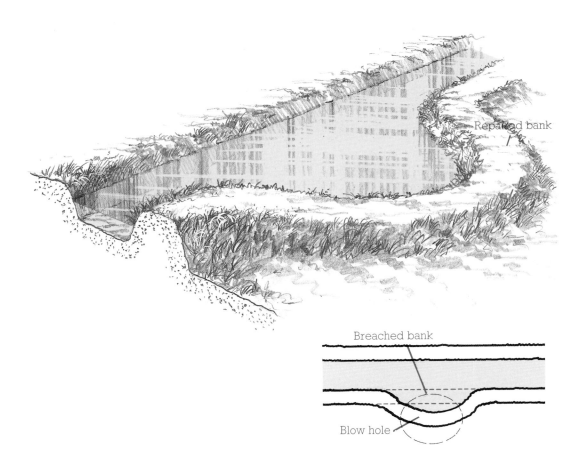

Size of watercourse >3 metres

Description Pond left after bank damage.

Purpose To create a wildlife habitat. There are no land-drainage benefits.

Method Where a flood bank has been breached, a scour hole is formed by the outrushing water. The subsequent bank repair can be formed around the scour hole in a horseshoe shape, thus leaving a deep pond connected to the drainage channel or alternatively the breach is mended leaving a deep pond on the landward side of the bank.

Conservation advantages Produces an area of marsh and standing water which can be colonised by plants and invertebrates. They also serve as a watering place for wild animals and birds and a breeding place for amphibia.

Option 17

Single plant fringe

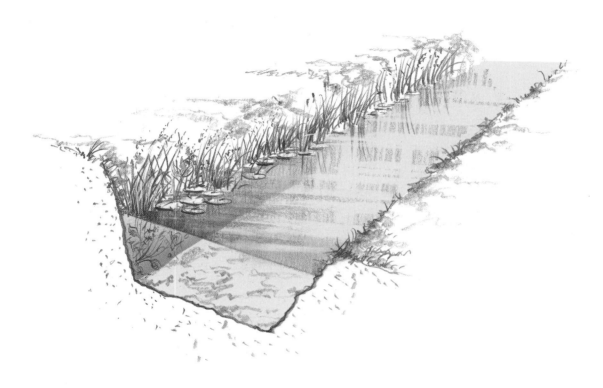

Size of watercourses All but the narrowest.

Description A fringe of emergent plants is retained at the base of one bank.

Purpose The benefit to land-drainage arises from bank stabilisation at its base which thus prevents scouring.

Method Selective dredging, working from one bank and leaving a fringe of emergents at the base of one bank. This option may not be appropriate for all parts of a watercourse.

Conservation advantages Retention of a stable emergent plant habitat with associated animals. Retention of sites for aquatic insects which use the reeds to change to their flying state. It also provides essential cover for fish fry. The retention of plants in a channel is also aesthetically pleasing.

Option 18

Double fringes of emergent plants

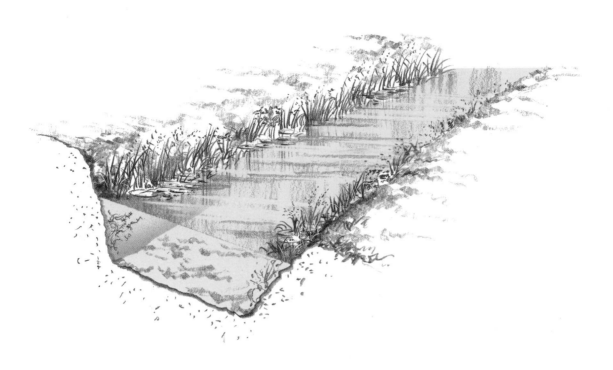

Size of watercourse >2 metres

Description A marginal strip of wetland emergent plants is left on both sides of the channel.

Purpose Banks can be stabilised at both their bases which prevents scouring or erosion and gives a benefit to land-drainage. This option may only be appropriate for short stretches of channel.

Method Selectively dredging or cutting the centre of a channel with a weed boat, leaving a narrow fringe of emergents on each side.

Conservation advantages Continuity of emergent plant species permits the establishment of an associated invertebrate community, provides structure for emerging aquatic insects enabling them to change to their aerial state. The plants also provide cover for fish fry. The presence of plants in a watercourse is also aesthetically pleasing.

Option 19

Control of emergents

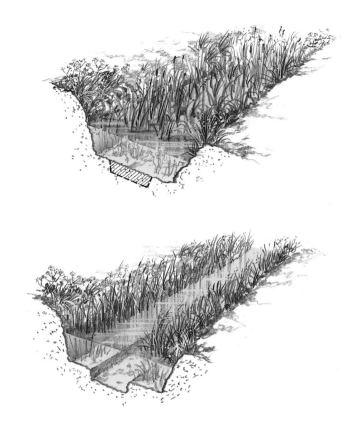

Size of watercourse Most. (Not successful where there is substantial movement of bed material or where there is little water.)

Description Management of aggressive emergent plants such as bulrush *Typha latifolia*.

Purpose Retention of the carrying capacity of a watercourse.

Method Overdeepening of the bed should prevent stands of adjacent shallow water emergents spreading into the deeper water. This option may not always be the most appropriate conservation management for aggressive plant species such as reed sweet-grass and reed canary-grass. This method does produce a berm within the existing channel which will be covered or exposed, dependent on the water level. Extra land-take will not be necessary but the berm can only be created if the channel has spare drainage capacity. Aquatic herbicides could be used to control the vegetation but the overdeepening creates greater habitat diversity.

Conservation advantages Retains the continuity of stands of emergent plants within the channel. This benefits invertebrates and provides potential fish spawning areas. It is a possible alternative to herbicide treatment.

Option 20

Submerged berm – method 1

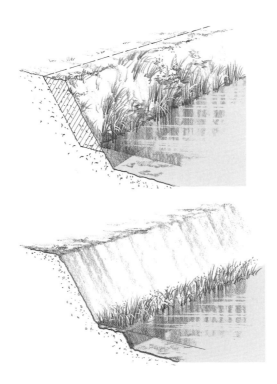

Size of watercourse >2 metres

Description A submerged berm is a narrow ledge formed at the base of the bank just below the normal summer water level and is usually covered with marsh plants. It can be created on one or both sides of the watercourse depending on the width of the channel. This may mean land-take but some farmers may be prepared to co-operate with the IDB or it could be possibly part of a set-aside option.

Purpose To support emergent plants whilst still maintaining a drainage function in the main channel. Although the channel capacity is increased during flood conditions, this option requires extra land take.

Method Form the berm working from the same bank. Remove existing vegetation and set aside for replanting or use spare vegetation from elsewhere. Favour plants such as common reed, bulrush, sedges and bur-reed rather than reed canary-grass and reed sweet-grass which can form uninteresting monocultures.

Conservation advantages Emergent plants are established in a range of water depths. These provide food for invertebrates and support for flying insects emerging from their aquatic state. A stable vegetation structure encourages water birds such as coot, little grebe and moorhen to breed. The different water depths will also favour different plants, creating diversity and habitat structure. It also provides food and shelter for fish fry.

Option 21

Submerged berm – method 2

1/3

Size of watercourse >2 metres

Description As for Option 20.

Purpose As for Option 20.

Method As for Option 20 but a margin of common reed is planted or encouraged through selective management. This should be encouraged to colonise up the bank behind and in front of the berm to give a broad linear reed-bed. See Option 22 concerning reed planting. Choose stretches of watercourse without adjacent trees or hedges as these can shade and depress reed growth and harbour predators. It may be possible for farmers entering the 'set-aside' scheme to use their land to create the berm.

Conservation advantages Creation of a linear reed-bed which is a decreasing habitat nationally. The wider the fringe, the greater the likelihood of attracting specialist reed nesting birds such as reed warblers. These birds like to nest over water but need the extra width of reed afforded by allowing it to grow up the banks to give protection from predators.

Option 22

Planting aquatics

Planting a reed-bed (reed is defined here as common reed *Phragmites australis*)

One of the great mistakes made in planting a reed-bed is to treat it as a wetland plant. Reed grows best, for example on the drier slopes of a bank. It will grow down into the water and root in the mud at a maximum water depth of approximately 0.5 metres. It will even form a floating mat.

Sown seed has a poor success rate. A cutting, containing a stem, rhizome and root ball will succeed best if planted in a damp soil. Attempts at establishing a reed-bed in waterlogged soil have a variable success rate. The cut end of a rhizome is very prone to fungal attack under wet conditions which can eventually kill the whole cutting.

Plant the cuttings approximately 30 centimetres to 1 metre apart depending on how quickly a dense reed-bed is required. The rhizome should be just covered with soil. Plant in late winter or early spring.

Planting other aquatics

Most rooted aquatic plants grow best at certain depths of water. Table 1 gives these preferred depths. Simply plant a root mat and stem, preferably in spring for best results. Most true aquatics will 'take' at all times of the year but it is best to avoid the winter months.

Introduction

Many different machines are used and some have been specifically designed to control plant growth on steep slopes. Banks are cut by the engineer for many reasons but the following are the most important –

☐ Relatively smooth banks have a low rugosity and improve the carrying capacity of the drain.

☐ Bank cutting stops the development of woody growth which would increase the rugosity of the channel. Tree roots on raised flood banks can create drainage paths which can weaken banks and result in flooding.

☐ Cutting encourages a matted root system and maximises the soil-binding qualities of the plant community, so reducing the risk of erosion or slippage.

☐ Burrowing animals can damage flood banks. They are deterred from colonising a trim bank because they are vulnerable to predation.

☐ Cut banks allow visual inspection of floodbanks.

☐ A trim bank is thought to be more attractive in an urban community.

☐ There is a legislative requirement to control noxious weeds and this must be undertaken as necessary.

Drainage channel banks appear very uniform but there are variations in width, aspect, slope, soil type and degrees of wetness. Even so, the ecological interest of a bank is mainly determined by different management practices. In turn the management practice is determined by the type of bank, its purpose and the consequence of its failure. High banks protecting property and extensive farm land must receive a high standard of maintenance but this can be reduced for lower banks.

A closely and regularly mown grass bank has little ecological interest but it might be highly desirable close to a village. Daisies, buttercups, clover and grasses dominate in what is essentially a lawn. Plants have very little chance of flowering and those that do are cut before setting seed. Insects and other invertebrates find little food and the lack of cover makes such banks totally unsuitable for mammals or nesting birds. However, moderate grazing by sheep can produce a more interesting sward. Their selectivity provides structure and form, promotes diversity and permits flowering.

Banks which are mown only in the autumn are entirely different but, even so, it is highly desirable that the cuttings are removed. If cuttings are left, the litter smothers the most sensitive plants and only coarse grasses survive. Litter removal also removes nutrients, so favouring many attractive herbs which are adapted to less rich soils. Herbs and grasses also have an opportunity to flower and set seed. The flowers can attract a host of insect life, from the obvious and colourful butterflies to the less obvious grasshoppers, beetles and weevils. The larvae of many butterflies and moths are very fussy, feeding on only one or two different kinds of plant. So, the greater the variety of plants, the greater the number of moths and butterflies. Typical and more attractive examples include the tortoiseshell and red admiral larvae which feed on the ubiquitous nettle, orange tip which feeds on hedge mustard, small copper which feeds on common sorrel and common blue which feeds on clover and vetches – see Table 2.

Tall grasses and low-growing herbs also provide a structure and difference of form which is preferred by mammals and ground nesting birds. Field vole, water vole and harvest mouse (its original habitat being stands of common reed) could feed on the numerous seeds, whilst the carnivorous common shrew and pygmy shrew feed on the invertebrate life.

Skylark, meadow pipit, reed bunting, pheasant and red-legged partridge could all be attracted to the different habitats provided by the different grasses and herbs.

Predators will exploit the now evident prey. On the ground fox, weasel and stoat will search for small mammals and birds, but overhead the skies could be patrolled by kestrel, little owl and the nocturnal tawny owl. Late evening and early morning could see barn owl quartering the ditches and in the winter the short-eared owl might be seen patrolling the banks.

If banks are mown less frequently than once a year, more coarse vegetation will dominate. Although the banks are less rich in wild flowers, birds such as whitethroat, willow warbler and sedge warbler will breed in the tall grasses and willow herb. Burdock, thistle, teasel, hogweed and knapweed are a rich seed source and are particularly attractive in the winter to goldfinch, linnet, yellowhammer and possibly brambling. Tall rank summer vegetation also provides a wind-break to weak flying insects such as alderflies and mayflies, thus becoming more attractive to hawking damselflies and dragonflies, bats and insectivorous birds such as warblers and spotted flycatchers.

Shrubby vegetation develops on those banks which are left uncut for periods greater than three years. Willow, alder, hazel, elderberry, hawthorn, blackthorn and bramble could invade the rank grasses, providing a variety of nesting sites for blackbird, song thrush, chaffinch, yellowhammer, hedge sparrow, linnet and even moorhen which likes to roost in hawthorn. Vegetation may have to be cut back or 'brushed' at infrequent intervals, otherwise a linear woodland will develop. As well as the shrubby vegetation being visually attractive, this different community of plants attracts its own range of animal life. Taken together, the three forms of bankside management provide a remarkable opportunity to increase the wildlife interest of the bank.

Permutations on these three types of management lead to even more interesting banks. For example, the lower half of the bank could be cut annually leaving the upper section for three years before cutting. Some lengths could be left to scrub over. Alternate banks could be cut annually or every three years. New banks or reprofiled banks may generate their own interesting flora from the seed bank. Some may benefit from a re-seed of low growing 'low maintenance' grass mixtures, or conservation seed mixes – see Table 4, whilst others could be re-seeded with mixtures from nearby SSSI hay meadows. All of these options and a full range of bankside management opportunities are considered in this chapter.

Management planning

Many of the bankside management opportunities should be planned so that the phasing of the different cuts does not become confused. In some cases a survey could be of value to identify existing habitats which could then be enhanced. For example, a bank which is scrubbed-over could be retained in part and maintained through appropriate management. Sections could be cleared allowing the development of grassland communities.

Most banksides will be grassed-over but these could be improved through different management practices or re-seeding. Attractive grassland banksides have many conservation advantages and low-growing, low-productivity grass mixtures require less management.

Many newly-formed banksides may still contain a relict seed bank of former low-productivity grasslands. It is a cheap and simple matter to have the seed bank checked by a competent botanist, but the seeds may take several weeks to germinate. Take soil samples from the site three to six months before the work commences. A lot of money could be saved using a natural seed source.

Newly-formed banks, and any banks which have to be sown with appropriate seed mixtures – see Table 4, need a planned cutting programme in the first three years. A spring and autumn cut will be needed as the exposed soil will provide ideal conditions for the colonisation or growth from the seed bank of the more aggressive weeds. Shading by these could kill the low-productivity grasses and herbs. Cutting removes the shading problem and allows the preferred species to establish and out-compete the more aggressive weeds. It is essential that the cuttings be removed, as this lowers the fertility of the soil, helping to change the rich soil environment, which again favours the growth of weed species.

Grazing intensity

At the end of the grazing season, aim for a sward with plants no less than seven centimetres high. As some plants will be more palatable to the stock than others there should be a variable height. This structure and form in the vegetation is vital to many invertebrates and ground nesting birds.

Option 23

Cutting techniques 1

Size of watercourse A larger watercourse provides greater flexibility in the adoption of any new mowing regime.

Description Use of grass cutting techniques to reduce its growth on the banks. Banks with specific interest will need to be identified when adopting a mowing regime.

Purpose The cuttings are removed so that the fertility of the bank soil is depleted. This favours less productive and more visually attractive plants without affecting the stability of the bank. Ultimately this should lead to a saving in annual maintenance costs.

Method Time the cut for July onwards if cutting for hay. Alternatively leave as late as possible so that the flowers can set seed, then cut and remove. Where these options are impracticable cut no earlier than June, with the more interesting banks scheduled for as late a cut as possible. The use of weed cutting buckets such as the Bradshaw or Herder machines ensures that the vegetation is removed so that the fertility of the bank soil is depleted. This favours less productive and more visually attractive plants without affecting the stability of the bank. Initially a spring and autumn cut may also be necessary until the dry matter production is reduced. However, disturbance to nesting birds and birds feeding their young, and the cutting of desirable plant species before they have time to flower and set seed, should be avoided.

Conservation advantages Plants of higher conservation interest will be favoured over species such as nettle, couch and false oat-grass. Desirable plants can increase by seeding. Established banks which have been re-seeded – see Table 4 – should not be cut before the middle of July, so as to simulate a traditional hay cut. Game birds are favoured by leaving cover.

Option 24

Cutting techniques 2

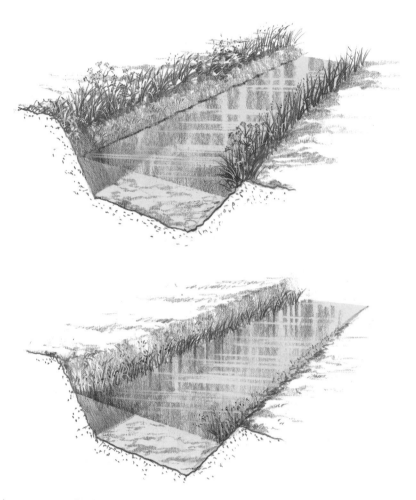

Size of watercourse All; but it could be an inappropriate method for very small channels.

Description Opportunity to leave parts of banks uncut for longer periods.

Purpose May speed up cutting programme.

Method Selectively remove vegetation on half the bank by (i) cutting and removing a strip above and just below the water level early in the season. Only cut the whole bank in the autumn. This could be achieved either by a machine from the bank or from a weed boat. Alternatively (ii) cut the bank at the break of the slope leaving a fringe of vegetation down the bank to the water's edge.

Conservation advantages Diversifies the habitat by having both long and short grass which favour different insects and mammals. Permits herbs to set seed before being cut. Gives cover to small mammals and encourages birds of prey.

Option 25

Cutting techniques 3 – reciprocating cutter plus rotary rake used to conservation advantage.

Size of watercourse 2 metres

Description Management of narrow channels.

Purpose This method provides fast economical management of vegetation in small drainage channels. The cutter can be mounted on a tractor, 'spider' or 'bicycle' machine depending on the ease of access. This method minimises crop damage.

Method The spider and bicycle machines require only a narrow strip of land on either side of the channel for access, as they both straddle it. A reciprocating blade cuts both bankside and marginal vegetation whilst the rotary rake removes cut vegetation to the top of the bank.

Conservation advantages This method of cutting is superior to flail mowing, if used for cutting banks only, as it removes the cut vegetation. It also can function as a hay cut if carried out after most flowers have set seed in July.

Banks

Option 26

Cutting techniques 3 – reciprocating cutter plus rotary rake, 'spider' or 'bicycle' machine, or the Bradshaw/Herder machine, used to no conservation advantage.

Size of watercourse 2 metres

Description Management of narrow channels.

Purpose The 'spider' or 'bicycle' machines provide a fast economical management of vegetation in small drainage channels. The Bradshaw or Herder machines provide an equally fast and economical management of vegetation, but they require a wider strip of land on the bank top for access.

Method The spider and bicycle machines only require a narrow strip of land on either side of the channel for access as they straddle it. A reciprocating blade in all examples cuts both bankside marginal and submerged vegetation.

Conservation advantages There are no particular conservation advantages when all machines are used in this way as they seriously damage the aquatic habitat. The Bradshaw or Herder machines can be used to the advantage of conservation if the cut is made above not below the root mat.

Option 27

Cutting techniques 4 – cutting by hand

Size of watercourse All

Description Use of personnel to manage sites by hand.

Purpose To deal with awkward sites or ones needing special management.

Method Cutting, and removing cut material to the top of the bank.

Conservation advantages Opportunity for managing special sites with more flexibility and sensitivity especially where timing is important. Possibility of leaving short stretches uncut by mechanical means to be cut later by hand after flowers have set seed.

Option 28

Cutting techniques 5 – hay cut

Size of watercourse All

Description The bankside grass is cut for hay.

Purpose The banks are managed commercially.

Method Cut for hay and remove as a crop preferably in July. This permits most herbs to mature and set seed if any are present. The crop should not be fertilised other than by grazing animals which return nutrients through grazing the aftermath. Unfertilised grass banks will eventually develop communities of low growing, low productivity grasses which also favour the colonisation by herbs. Such communities could be introduced through re-seeding – see Table 4 and introduction to this chapter.

Conservation advantages An opportunity to restore herb-rich grassland through re-seeding or appropriate management. Nationally these grassland habitats are scarce. Such management allows herbs to seed and increase at the expense of coarse plants which gives cover and food for small mammals and insects.

Option 29

Cutting techniques 6 – silage cut

Size of watercourse Applies more generally to the larger watercourses.

Description Commercial use of grass banks which have less than a 30 degree angle to permit use of a forage harvester.

Purpose Cutting costs are eliminated.

Method Regular silage cut from banks according to productivity. No additional fertiliser should be applied.

Conservation advantages When combined with other forms of bank management, gives an added habitat, although few plants or animals benefit from this form of intensive management. Regular cutting tends to create a monoculture. Cutting for hay encourages a diversity of plants and is therefore preferable.

Option 30

Cutting techniques 7 – flail mowing

Size of watercourse All

Description Flail mowing of banks.

Purpose The bank is managed with a robust, easy to use machine.

Method Use of a tractor-mounted flail on the bankside vegetation. The macerated material is left *in situ*. Uncollected debris tends to fall into the waterway, impeding flow and necessitating more frequent dredging.

Conservation advantages There are no conservation advantages. The cut material smothers the less robust constituents of the vegetation and recycles nutrients on site encouraging dense vegetation growth and higher production. Should not be undertaken before mid-July, so avoiding the destruction of nesting birds, their young and their food supply.
  The cut material will also enrich the aquatic habitat which could in time change and simplify the community to the detriment of conservation interest.

Option 31

Grazing

Size of watercourse >2 metres. If unfenced, the edges of smaller watercourses will be trampled and may require more frequent reprofiling.

Description Management by animals.

Purpose To reduce the problems of long term maintenance on the larger watercourses only, although fencing may be an additional cost.

Method The banks are grazed using cattle on the larger drains and sheep or cattle on the smaller drains. Horses on their own graze selectively so need to be mixed with cattle. All animals can cause problems if the land is overstocked. Land needs to be rested periodically.

Conservation advantages Reduces the dominance of coarse vegetation such as nettle and false oat-grass and favours a more open sward into which herbs can be introduced to add diversity if desired. Short grass and dung will be favoured by many invertebrates, and low intensity grazing provides form and structure to the sward, encouraging feeding and roosting areas for birds. See paragraph on *Grazing intensity* at the beginning of this chapter. Treading of channel margins can encourage more attractive aquatic emergents and will encourage the growth of annual wetland edge plants.

Banks

Option 32

Natural regeneration of banks

Size of watercourse All

Description Re-creation of natural grasslands on channel banks.

Purpose To stabilise bare soil on banks.

Method Many newly-formed banksides may still contain a relict seed bank of former low-productivity grasslands. It is a cheap and simple matter to have the seed bank checked by a competent botanist, but the seeds may take several weeks to germinate. Take soil samples from the site three to six months before the work commences. A lot of money could be saved using a natural seed source. Allow the seeds to grow from the new bank, but cut in the spring and autumn for two years and thereafter revert to an autumn cut. Remove the cuttings.

Conservation advantages The seed bank, over the years, may have lost some sensitive seeds but most of the original stock should be present. This method will restore a proportion of the original bankside flora and may in part, be similar to old meadow floras which have long since been turned to arable fields.

Option 33

Re-seeding banks

Size of watercourse All

Description Re-creation of natural grasslands on channel banks.

Purpose To stabilise bare soil on banks. Although the initial cost of the seed of low productivity grasses may be greater, the long term maintenance costs should be reduced, as dry matter production will be less. Alternatively, banks can be re-seeded with hay seed mixtures from hay-meadow SSSIs.

Method As the surfaces to be re-seeded are likely to be sloping, it will be impossible to prepare a standard seedbed. However, bank faces should be roughened by using a bucket with teeth or by chain harrowing, to permit seeds to lodge and avoid rolling down to the base of the slope. The seed will have to be either broadcast or introduced in a sowing medium. The latter will increase the cost but should ensure a better take. Sowing mediums include such substances as a foam based on woodpulp, sand, sawdust and agricultural meal. They are suitable for small areas with high visual amenity. For short stretches, pot-grown plants of showy species such as cowslip can be planted. Further spread will then be by seed. In all cases cut in the spring and autumn for two years and thereafter revert to an autumn cut. Remove the cuttings.

Conservation advantages It is calculated that 95% of the country's diverse grasslands have been lost in land-use changes to arable and more intensive grass leys. This reduction has had a knock-on effect on insects such as moths and butterflies. The establishment of stretches of grassland with mixed grasses and herbs will offer opportunities for insects to re-extend their range and frequency – see Tables 2 and 3. The disadvantage of this option is that larvae may be swept away by summer floods. See Table 4 for a general purpose seed mix.

Banks

Option 34

Buffer strips on the bank tops

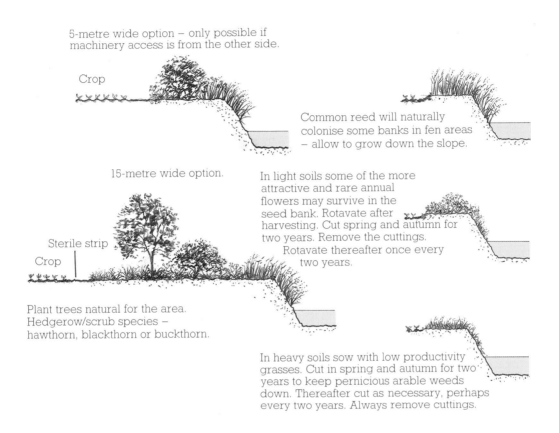

5-metre wide option – only possible if machinery access is from the other side.

Crop

Common reed will naturally colonise some banks in fen areas – allow to grow down the slope.

15-metre wide option.

In light soils some of the more attractive and rare annual flowers may survive in the seed bank. Rotavate after harvesting. Cut spring and autumn for two years. Remove the cuttings. Rotavate thereafter once every two years.

Sterile strip

Crop

Plant trees natural for the area. Hedgerow/scrub species – hawthorn, blackthorn or buckthorn.

In heavy soils sow with low productivity grasses. Cut in spring and autumn for two years to keep pernicious arable weeds down. Thereafter cut as necessary, perhaps every two years. Always remove cuttings.

Size of watercourse All

Description Guidelines for adjacent agricultural activity.

Purpose To promote long term stability of the bank slope and to protect those habitats created on them. It would also create an access strip for bicycle mowers.

Method A Code of Conduct is agreed between the IDB and the farming members. It is suggested that it take the form of leaving a minimum of one metre of land unploughed and untreated with chemicals adjacent to the watercourse. The strip could be sown and included in the cutting regime for the banks once a year. Some farmers may wish to enter into the set-aside scheme financed by central government. A 15 metre strip on the top of a bank could be re-seeded or re-constructed as a low productivity grassland.

Conservation advantages The banks of greatest wildlife interest are those where the soil is impoverished in agricultural terms. Leaving a top strip untreated with herbicide or fertiliser acts as a buffer zone to the bank slope. Not ploughing close to the edge also prevents the bank from becoming destabilised. Repair work is reduced which thus reduces the disturbance to the wildlife on the bank. Such a strip could also provide game cover for a farm.

Banks

Option 35

Retention of vertical banks

Use a hazel hurdle (willow could re-grow).

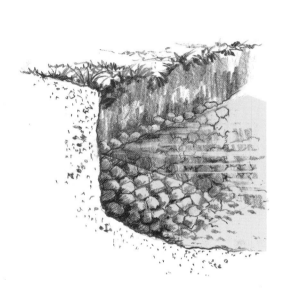

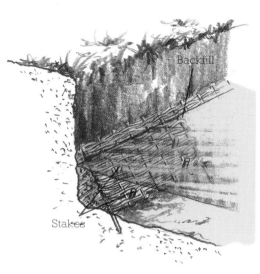

Size of watercourse Shallow channels >2 metres. More applicable to natural watercourses.

Description Occasionally an IDB may control more natural watercourses. Where possible, retain physical features such as vertical banks or meanders.

Purpose To foster wildlife. There is no land-drainage function.

Method Vertical banks occur on bends, or below weirs and culverts. If the bank is receding into land of no consequence then it could be left to follow its natural course. If it is necessary to stabilise it then this can be done by deflecting the current away from the toe of the bank and protecting the bank with stones or staked wattles – see next five Options. Avoid using vertical asbestos or steel sheet piling as these destroy habitats.

Conservation advantages Keeps potential nesting sites for kingfishers and sand martins. It is also valuable for solitary bees.

Banks

Option 36

Stabilising banks by using faggots

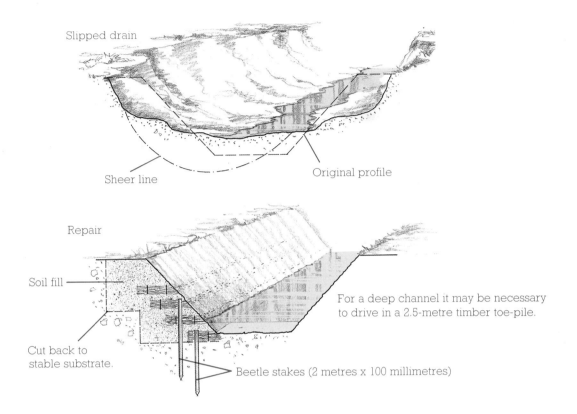

Slipped drain

Sheer line

Original profile

Repair

Soil fill

Cut back to stable substrate.

For a deep channel it may be necessary to drive in a 2.5-metre timber toe-pile.

Beetle stakes (2 metres x 100 millimetres)

Size of watercourse All

Description Bundles of wood are used for bank stabilisation and slip repairs.

Purpose To repair a reprofiled bank that has slipped or to stabilise a bank liable to slippage, when constructed for example over running silt.

Method Faggots from hawthorn or fruit trees can be prepared in winter and stored. A faggot is traditionally about one metre long, 30 centimetres in diameter and bound into bundles. When carrying out a repair first remove bank material to three or four faggot's depth from the desired profile and store. Lay a line of faggots vertically up the bank and just below bed level. Cover with soil then lay a second line offset to give the correct profile. Stake at intervals with 1.2 to 1.8 metre stakes. Cover with soil and repeat to give three or four layers of faggots, finishing with soil.

Conservation advantages A profiled bank stabilised with faggots has more value for wildlife than a vertical bank stabilised with steel or asbestos sheet piling. There is also a spin off for wildlife where hedges are planted and maintained especially for providing faggots.

Banks

Option 37

Stabilising banks using wattle

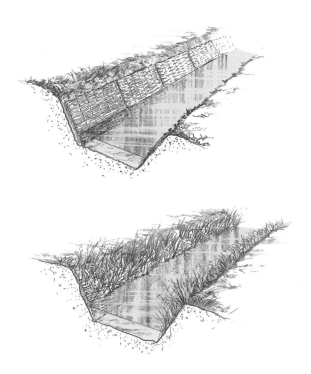

Size of watercourse All

Description Use of pliable wood to shield banks from the effects of scour.

Purpose To stabilise the toe of a bank subject to erosion. Some concern has been expressed about the safety of steel sheet or asbestos piling. Long lines of vertical banks are dangerous. People and animals falling in cannot easily climb out. The free access of wildlife from the bank to the water is also curtailed. The use of natural materials often provides a suitable alternative. Natural materials also give greater flexibility than piling in engineering terms, as the latter are difficult to remove in, for example, channel enlargements.

Method Drive stakes, more than two metres long into the base of the bank in a staggered double row. Weave freshly-cut (and therefore pliable) branches of willow or hazel between them to a height above the highest expected water level. Fill in with soil behind and plant to stabilise the surface. Willow stakes will sprout if used, which would give greater protection to a toe particularly affected by scour. Alternatively, scoops of common reed (not bur-reed) can be placed in front of the wattle to establish a plant fringe and deflect the current.

Conservation advantages Natural materials for bank stabilisation are preferable to concrete finishes, steel piling or stone gabions as they present more opportunities for interesting plant and animal communities to develop. They provide free access for animals.

Banks

Option 38

Stabilising banks using trees

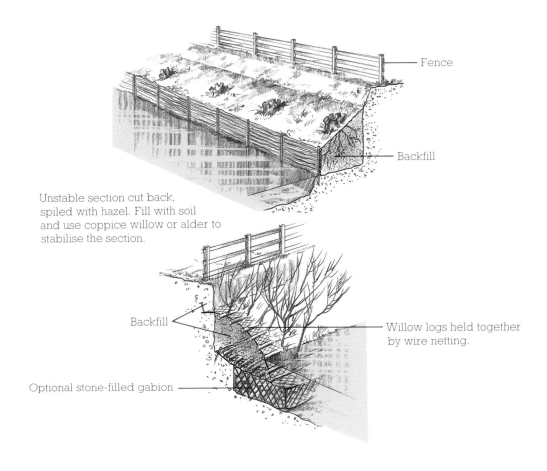

Fence

Backfill

Unstable section cut back, spiled with hazel. Fill with soil and use coppice willow or alder to stabilise the section.

Backfill

Willow logs held together by wire netting.

Optional stone-filled gabion

Size of watercourse All. More opportunities arise in natural watercourses.

Description Selective planting and management of woody species.

Purpose To protect banks from erosion or collapse in a friable soil.

Method Trees and shrubs have extensive root systems which bind soil. Alder is the best species for planting at the base of the bank in small watercourses. Willow is as effective and more easily established but is too bushy for small channels.

Planting can also be done at the top of the bank. A vertical bank caused through scouring below weirs is one feature which could be protected by tree planting. Smaller trees such as hawthorn or sallow would be preferable to larger trees such as ash – see Table 5. Manage through selective pruning.

Conservation advantages Retains trees along a watercourse benefiting birds, bats and invertebrates. Vertical banks are attractive to kingfishers, sand martins and solitary bees.

Banks

Option 39

Stabilising banks using stones

Size of watercourse All

Description Use of stone to stabilise banks.

Purpose This method deflects or reduces the erosive power of water against banks and stabilises slips in running silt or sand.

Method Stone at the toe of an undercut bank reduces the impact of the current and stabilises the bank. Large stones bind together better and are not moved by the current.

Conservation advantages Permits retention of vertical banks as possible kingfisher nesting sites. Vertical asbestos and sheet piling will destroy the habitat.

Banks

Option 40

Stabilising banks using prefabricated materials

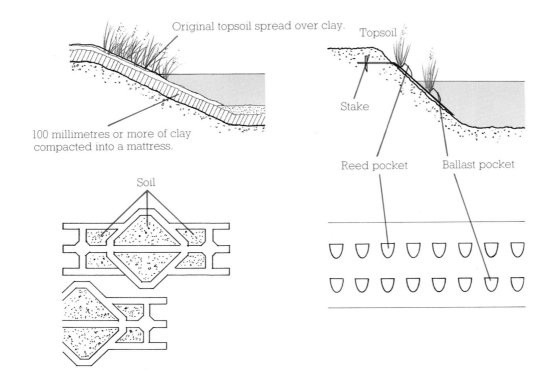

Original topsoil spread over clay.

100 millimetres or more of clay compacted into a mattress.

Topsoil

Stake

Reed pocket

Ballast pocket

Soil

Size of watercourse All

Description Materials presently on the market include flexible mats of pre-cast concrete blocks, interlocking concrete shapes, mats of bitumen-impregnated geotextiles and biodegradable mats of natural fibre sown with appropriate plant species, all to order.

Purpose To protect banks subject to scour or slippage such as those in sand and running silt.

Method Lay out the mat units and stake in position. The flexible nature of the mat enables it to fit the contours of the site. The toe of the mat must be below the base of the bank to prevent it being undermined, and the top of the mattress above the top water level. This method of repair is rapid, has a long but measurable life span but is itself difficult to repair if it shifts or is undermined. In this respect it is not as effective as faggoting. Machinery used for desilting has to be used very carefully so as not to catch and lift the mat.

Conservation advantages There are limited conservation advantages over alternative methods such as faggoting, although some materials are specifically designed to encourage vegetation. The use of these materials is an improvement on banks that have been faced with concrete or stone walls, as plants are able to grow through the mats. It would be possible to sow conservation mixes on these sites.

Banks

Option 41

Bank cover – scrub

Size of watercourse All. Not applicable in channels taking high flood flows or in channels less than five metres wide.

Description Discrete patches of dense low cover.

Purpose Would serve to suppress invasion of banks by undesirable tree species such as sycamore if adjacent to a plantation; otherwise of no direct land-drainage benefit.

Method Encouragement or planting of suitable species such as bramble and blackthorn to form discrete blocks of dense cover on banks. This option could be incorporated with one encouraging bankside trees and these will act as look-outs for predators. Such sites can also encourage rabbits so the siting could be critical.

Conservation advantages Such thickets are valuable as a terrestrial habitat for frogs, toads and newts. Dense cover also benefits the larger mammals such as fox, badger, otter and stoat. It also favours the larger waterbirds such as moorhens and possibly mallard. Scrub and bramble thickets are suitable breeding habitats for birds like whitethroats, blackbirds, wrens, song thrushes, blue tits, great tits, robins and many others. The presence of small songbirds may in turn encourage bird predators such as sparrow hawks and owls.

Option 42

Pollarding willows

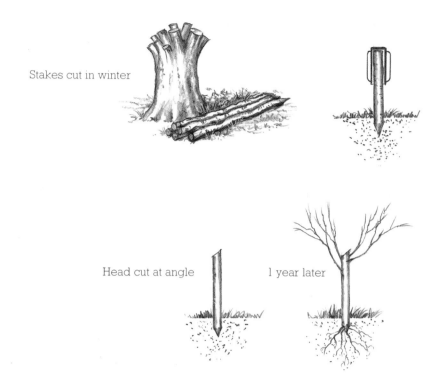

Stakes cut in winter

Head cut at angle   1 year later

Size of watercourse All

Description The cutting of crack or white willow trees rather than shrub willows at a height of approximately two metres to encourage a broom headed appearance.

Purpose To foster wildlife. There is no direct land-drainage benefit although willow roots are good bank stabilisers.

Method Many pollards already exist and re-pollarding is a matter of cutting back each pollard to the top of the trunk to prevent the crown rotting out. Theoretically, any tree can be pollarded, although willow is the usual species. New willow trees can be planted using stakes. These should preferably be 20 centimetres in diameter and cut at the top at an oblique angle to shed water and prevent rotting. The stake should be three metres long with a metre planted into the ground. A height of two metres is necessary if machinery or stock are to have access to the bank base. Pollards of a lower height may be appropriate elsewhere.

Conservation advantages Willows are rich in invertebrates which attract bats and birds to feed as well as to roost. They are also aesthetically pleasing and are associated with the fenland scene where they traditionally acted as markers for fenland roads at times of flood.

Banks

Option 43

Trimming of overhanging branches

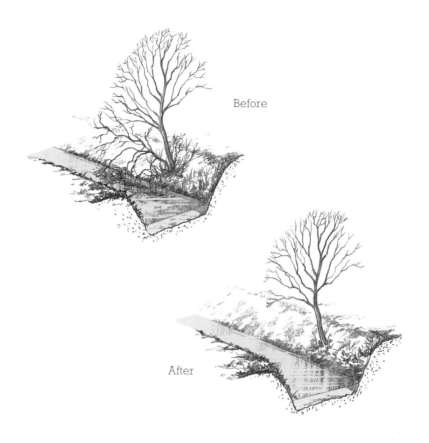

Before

After

Size of watercourse All

Description Selective removal of lower branches which overhang the watercourse and catch flood debris.

Purpose The selective removal of branches reduces maintenance costs. Shading of the watercourse is retained so suppressing weed growth. Fish will continue to benefit from the invertebrates that fall into the water from the foliage.

Method Remove only those branches which overhang the water and are actively affecting water-flow. Cut cleanly close to the trunk or main branch and avoid leaving snags or torn bark. It is good practice to seal the cuts with a recommended commercial sealant.

Conservation advantages Trees and shrubs provide food and/or shelter for wildlife. The type of tree is often important. Native species have the richest invertebrate fauna. Some, such as willow and alder, are adapted to growing in damp situations and others, such as oak and ash, have extensive root systems that both bind the banks and can provide features like otter holts, bat roosts and bird nesting sites for wildlife – see Table 5.

Option 44

Working between trees

Size of watercourse All

Description The retention of selected bankside trees and the removal of others for machine access to the channel.

Purpose In some situations shade will act as a useful management tool by depressing undesirable weed growth; also some tree species stabilise banks with their roots. This option may not be appropriate for all sites.

Method Where there is no alternative, carefully select trees for removal so as to permit access for machinery to function efficiently.

Conservation advantages The retention of mature or sapling trees supports birds and invertebrates – see Table 5 for suitable types. They may also be the only trees present in an intensive agricultural landscape and they can be aesthetically pleasing, breaking up the monotony of a large field. Invertebrates falling from overhanging branches may act as fish food.

Option 45

Coppicing

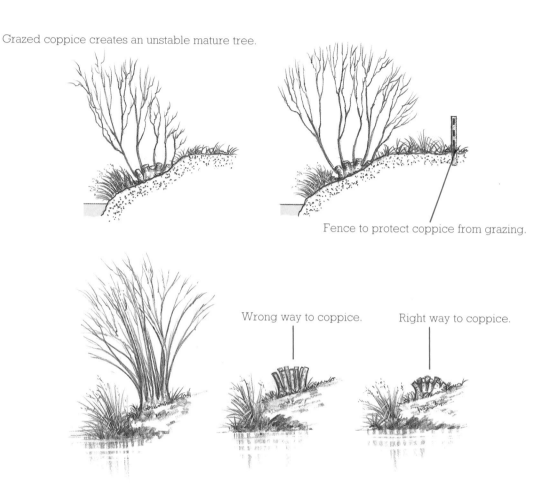

Grazed coppice creates an unstable mature tree.

Fence to protect coppice from grazing.

Wrong way to coppice.   Right way to coppice.

Size of watercourse All

Description Rotational coppicing of shrubs and young trees where access for machinery is necessary.

Purpose The practice facilitates access for machinery. There is an additional long-term management cost, if coppicing replaces the selective removal of trees – see Option 44, although coppice material may be saleable in some districts.

Method Cut trunks close to the ground using a slanting cut which sheds rainwater. Branches regenerate from the base or 'stool'.

Conservation advantages Coppiced shrub retains cover by watercourses for birds and invertebrates. Moorhens roost in low branches and use dense shrubs as protection from predators.

Banks

Option 46

Singling coppice

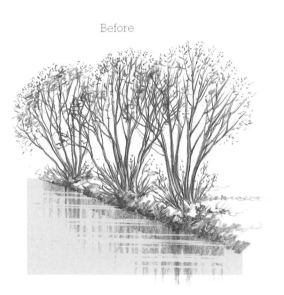
Before

After

Size of watercourse All

Description Selection of single coppice stems to form trees.

Purpose This improves access to the channel for machinery. It allows more light into the watercourse and decreases the volume of material to be disposed of during maintenance coppicing.

Method The removal of trees and shrubs from a bank will de-stabilise it and the use of a herbicide on stumps to kill the roots may have the same results. Coppicing was a common alternative. However, this gives a multi-stemmed bush or tree which may present a problem for access in the future. The selection of one or more vigorous stems growing at a suitable angle away from the channel and the removal of the rest will result in a dominant trunk that will be easier to work around. The resulting tree can be pollarded or recoppiced at some future date.

Conservation advantages The tree and shrub cover is retained whilst permitting more light into the watercourse.

Banks

Option 47

Hedgerow planting

Staggered double row hedge planted for stock barrier and material for faggots.

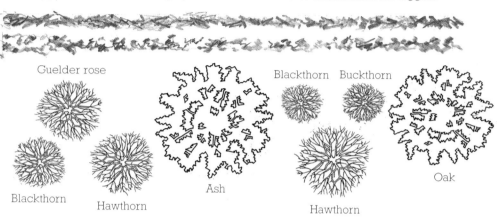

Guelder rose

Blackthorn Buckthorn

Blackthorn

Hawthorn

Ash

Hawthorn

Oak

Bank could be planted to increase habitat diversity – avoid straight lines.

Drainage channel

Size of watercourse All. Applicable where the adjoining land is owned by a drainage authority.

Description Planting a hedge.

Purpose To provide material for faggots, provide a habitat for wildlife and enhance the landscape.

Method Rotovate or similarly prepare the ground for planting. Hawthorn whips (that is, plants half a metre in height) should be planted half a metre apart in a staggered double row 30 centimetres apart.

Conservation advantages The hedge provides an extra habitat for nesting birds, and a nectar source for insects. It also provides a natural material for bank reinforcement. If possible plant the hedge on the north side. Alternatively plant on the east or west side, but not on both banks. Avoid planting on the south side as many insects prefer an open southerly aspect for flying in and out.

Option 48

Laying hedges

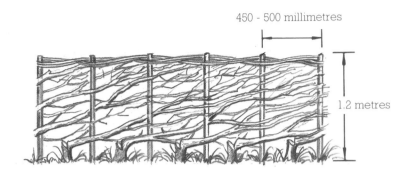

Detail of plaiting at the top of the hedge.

Size of watercourse All

Description The laying of channel-side hedges in the traditional fashion.

Purpose Permits easier access for hydraulic machinery which can work over the top of the hedge. Laying a hedge prolongs its working life and keeps it stock proof.

Method Use traditional hedge-laying techniques. Professional hedgelayers still exist and voluntary bodies such as the British Trust for Conservation Volunteers have groups of trained volunteers. In some situations select suitable tree stems in the hedge and leave uncut. Or plant ash saplings in the hedge. Both will provide a standard tree.

Conservation advantages More light will enter the watercourse and this will be an advantage where aquatic plant growth is desirable. Periodic laying also prolongs the life of the hedge, thickens the bottom and provides cover for moorhens and song birds.

Banks

Option 49

Manipulation of shading

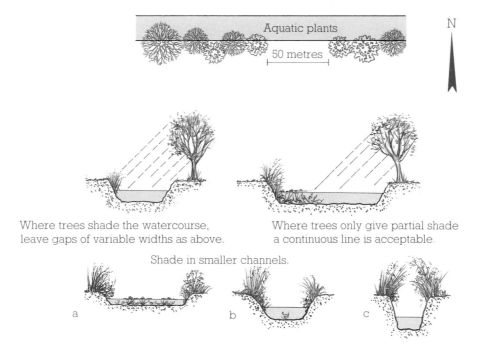

Shade in major drainage channels.

Aquatic plants

50 metres

N

Where trees shade the watercourse, leave gaps of variable widths as above.

Where trees only give partial shade a continuous line is acceptable.

Shade in smaller channels.

a   b   c

The effect of shade on aquatic plants as the channel width reduces. In c the channel is completely shaded even if orientated in a north-south direction.

Size of watercourse All

Description The use of shaded and unshaded sections of bank, to depress or eliminate aquatic plant growth in the shaded section and encourage plant growth in the unshaded section.

Purpose The only direct benefit to land-drainage would be if it were necessary to reduce water-speed because of local erosion of banks or flooding downstream.

Method Creating shade is well known as a method by which plant growth can be depressed or eliminated. However, too much shading will reduce the conservation interest of a watercourse, making it uniform. If plants die, aquatic refuges for fish fry and invertebrates are also lost. A balance of open and shaded sections is usually adequate for effective land-drainage. Even dappled shade may be sufficient in some instances to permit some aquatic plant growth without the channel becoming choked.

Conservation advantages Partial shading creates a diversity of habitat within the channel which can encourage a richer plant and animal community.

Option 50

Introduction of bushes and trees

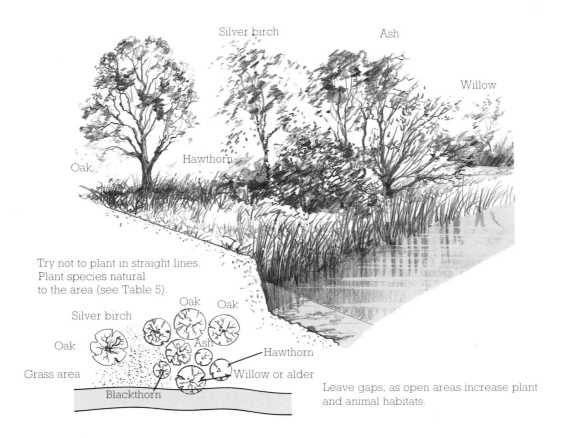

Size of watercourse Large fen drains are particularly appropriate although not where these carry water at a level higher than the adjacent land.

Description Introduction of trees and shrubs to diversify the habitat.

Purpose To foster wildlife. There is no land drainage advantage.

Method Some very large channels with banks of two metres or more have little or no shrub or tree cover. As the changes in water level in these channels are generally not as extreme as in natural watercourses, the presence of shrub cover should not affect run-off unduly. However, only one side should be allowed to develop scrub, leaving one side for access. Try and keep the south side free. Alternatively choose the east or west sides, but not both. Other possible sites could include those channels close to the watershed where there is minimal flow.

Conservation advantages It introduces a diversity of habitat and structure to a fairly uniform landscape. However, scrub should not be developed in these areas to the detriment of already established reed-beds or herb-rich grassland.

Banks

Option 51

Planting of trees or shrubs at drain junctions

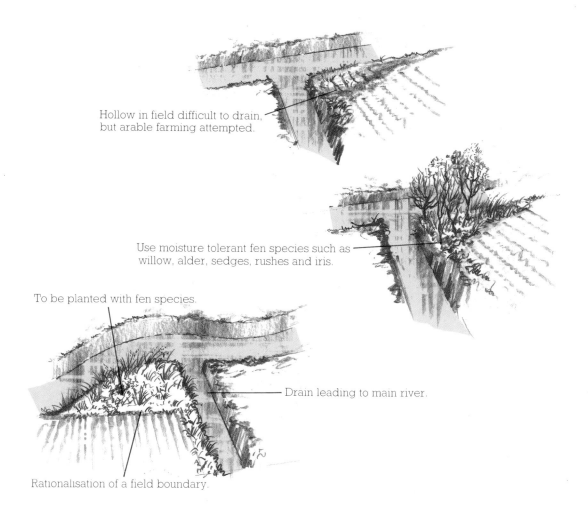

Hollow in field difficult to drain, but arable farming attempted.

Use moisture tolerant fen species such as willow, alder, sedges, rushes and iris.

To be planted with fen species.

Drain leading to main river.

Rationalisation of a field boundary.

Size of watercourse All

Description Planting of trees and shrubs at drain junctions.

Purpose To foster wildlife. There is no land-drainage advantage.

Method At the junctions of drainage channels, plant up awkward corners that are difficult to cultivate. This should not be coupled with the creation of pools at the same site or it will impede maintenance machinery.

Conservation advantages Adds diversity of habitat to areas of arable land where few trees and shrubs remain. Suitable species for planting are discussed in Table 5.

Option 52

Flood storage reservoirs or washlands

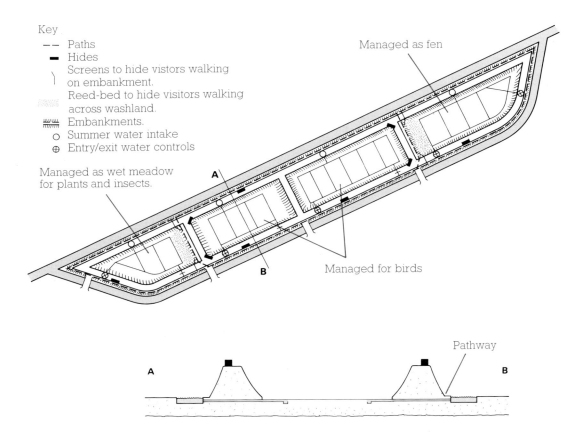

Key
- ── Paths
- ▬ Hides
- ⟍ Screens to hide vistors walking on embankment.
- Reed-bed to hide visitors walking across washland.
- ⅏ Embankments.
- ○ Summer water intake
- ⊕ Entry/exit water controls

Managed as fen

Managed as wet meadow for plants and insects.

A

B

Managed for birds

Pathway

A   B

Size of watercourse All may have potential although the larger watercourses are the most likely to have insufficient drainage capacity.

Description A large storage area often enclosed by drainage channels and their banks.

Purpose To provide a temporary storage area for channels prone to flooding. This reduces the cost of capital works to the channel by permitting flooding to take place on a fairly regular basis.

Method Identify sites where the storage of water during high water conditions will reduce the chances of flooding downstream. Create low flood banks at a distance from the channel or higher ones closer to it. The management of land within this flood plain would usually be for grazing.

Conservation advantages The creation of new washlands has enormous potential for conservation. Grassland, particularly wet grassland, has been reduced as a habitat in all parts of the country and the re-creation or encouragement of such sites would benefit breeding birds, plant and invertebrate life, and the winter feeding of waders and wildfowl.

Option 53

Management of drove roads

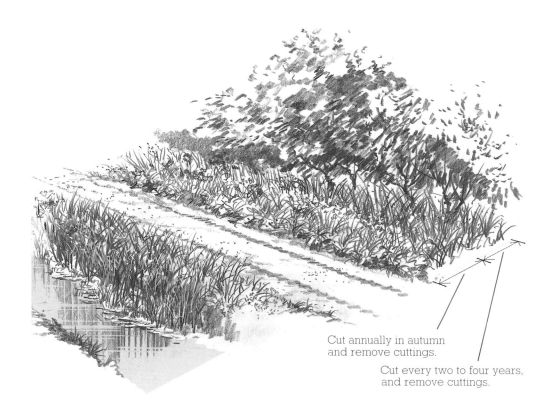

Cut annually in autumn
and remove cuttings.

Cut every two to four years,
and remove cuttings.

Size of watercourse All

Description All access roads, some of which are of historic interest.

Purpose To foster wildlife. There is no land-drainage advantage.

Method In some instances channels are bordered by earth tracks or 'droves'. These may be managed by an IDB, for a farmer, possibly as a courtesy gesture or for access. Management by cutting with a reciprocating cutter with the removal of cut material is the ideal management. Also the timing of the cut and the number of cuts per year can be manipulated to increase the plant and insect interest – see paragraphs at the beginning of this chapter.

Conservation advantages A drove that is cut once only, towards autumn, will develop short, medium and tall herbage during the following summer. This single cut encourages a greater diversity of plants and insects. A 'wood edge' habitat can be created along the edge of the grass strip by not cutting for two to four years and allowing it to scrub over. This will encourage a different community of birds, insects, particularly butterflies, and mammals such as field mice and bats.

Option 54

Creation of willow carr

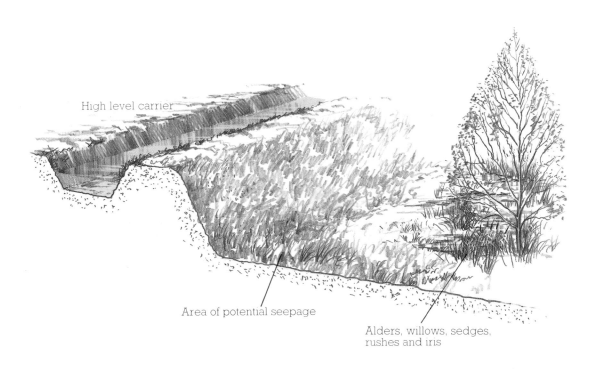

High level carrier

Area of potential seepage

Alders, willows, sedges, rushes and iris

Size of watercourse Those carriers which are above the adjacent land.

Description Water may seep through the base of a bank providing an excellent habitat for the development of wet vegetation.

Purpose To dry out wet areas caused by water seepage.

Method High level carriers occasionally lose water through ground water seepage giving a wet area at the base of the bank outside the channel. The planting of these areas with willow or alders will help dry out the area by transpiration through the leaves. It is essential that the trees are not planted close to the bank as the roots may weaken it.

Conservation advantages Creates small patches of wet woodland in areas where such habitat is scarce. Birds in particular would benefit, attracting more species to the area because of the cover, feeding and ultimately nesting opportunities. At one site, fen vegetation is developing within the willow carr with iris and sedges providing more habitats for insect and bird life.

Table 2 Butterflies

By encouraging the appropriate food plants for caterpillars, nectar plants for adults and in some cases scrub for sheltered flight, conditions for the following butterflies can be created.

Plants	Brimstone	Common blue	Gatekeeper	Large skipper	Meadow brown	Orange-tip	Wall brown
Wild grasses			★	★	★		★
Bird's-foot-trefoil/ black medick/vetches		★					
Lady's smock						★	
Watercress						★	
Hedge mustard						★	
Buckthorn (alder and purging)	★						
Scrub for shelter	★		★	★			

Table 3 Moths

Night flying and day flying moths will also benefit from the provision of larval food plants, a nectar source and shelter.

Plants	Bulrush moth	Eyed hawk	Herald moth	Marsh carpet†	Puss moth	Sallow moth	Sallow kitten	Six-spot burnet
Bird's-foot-trefoil								★
Meadow rue				★				
Bulrush	★							
Sallow		★	★		★	★	★	
Willow		★	★		★	★	★	

† Unlike the other moths listed, this moth is very local in its occurrence. It is found with its food plant on drain banks on the Nottinghamshire/Lincolnshire border. Its continued survival is largely dependent on the sympathetic management of these banks.

Table 4 Re-seeding banks with low productivity plants

There is increasing interest in reducing the cost of grassland maintenance and in the creation of grassland that is both aesthetically pleasing and of value for wildlife as such there is an increasing demand for 'conservation' seed mixes. The supply of seed is increasing because of the demand and prices are becoming competitive, although productive 'agricultural' grasses are less expensive. A number of the grasses, recommended below, are available commercially for sport's turfs such as golf courses and bowling greens for which specific qualities have been bred for and are 'named' varieties.

Grass	Qualities
Crested dog's-tail *Cynosurus cristatus*	Short, tufted, likes poor conditions, low productivity
Common bent-grass *Agrostis capillaris* synonym: *A. tenuis*	Likes poor conditions, rhizomes, good binding quality

Highland bent-grass *Agrostis castellana* (foreign) is cheaper and is usually sold instead of *A. capillaris* in mixes. It is relatively productive and hence very invasive, with vigorous rhizomes and stolons. In contrast with the native species it is taller, more productive, has poor summer colour but is very green in winter.

Grass	Qualities
Flattened meadow-grass *Poa compressa*	Stress tolerant, rhizomes, low productivity
Golden hair-grass *Trisetum flavescens*	Stress tolerant, tufted, low productivity, attractive
Slender creeping red fescue *Festuca rubra*	Good binding quality, low productivity
Chewings fescue *Festuca rubra* ssp *commutata*	Stress tolerant, tufted, low productivity

Ordinary creeping red fescue (ssp *rubra*) has good binding ability but will swamp herbs if sown in any quantity. The use of slender creeping red fescue such as ssp *pruinosa* or ssp *litoralis* and/or Chewings fescue (ssp *commutata*) gives good binding properties with lower productivity.

Grass	Qualities
Sheep's-fescue *Festuca ovina*	Tufted, drought resistant, low productivity, wide adaptivity to pH
Sweet vernal-grass *Anthoxanthum odoratum*	Short, tufted, likes poor conditions, low productivity, attractive

Herbs	Qualities	Flowering
Bird's-foot-trefoil *Lotus corniculatus*	Food plant of common blue butterfly and six spot-burnet. A tufted legume. It has little enriching effect unlike white and suckling clovers which should be avoided.	May-Sept
Common cat's-ear* *Hypochoeris radicata*	Good nectar/pollen source, bright yellow flowers, rosette	June-Sept
Cowslip *Primula veris*	Early pollen source, spreads readily once established, rosette	April-May
Selfheal *Prunella vulgaris*	Generally short, pollen and nectar source	June-Sept
Oxeye daisy *Leucanthemum vulgare*	Nectar source, aesthetically pleasing, readily established on neutral to basic soils	June-Aug
Upright hedge-parsley** *Torilis japonica*	Annual, but seeds readily. Medium height, attractive	July-Aug
Wild carrot *Daucus carota*	Does well on neutral to basic soils. Good nectar/pollen source, biennial, deep rooted, medium height.	June-Aug
Yarrow *Achilles millefolium*	Medium height, nectar source, deep rooted	June-Aug

  * Autumn hawkbit *Leontodon autumnalis* and rough hawkbit *Leontodon hispidus* are good alternatives when seed is in short supply.
** Native form preferred but agricultural form acceptable.

Grasses

Standard seed mix	Simple seed mix
%	%
40 Sheep's-fescue	50 Sheep's-fescue
15 Slender creeping red fescue	20 Slender creeping red fescue
15 Crested dog's-tail	10 Common bent-grass
15 Sweet vernal-grass	20 Mixed herbs
10 Flattened meadow-grass	
5 Common bent-grass	

Herbs

Herbs usually have deep tap roots whilst grasses are surface rooted. A proportion of herbs in a mix promotes extra bank stability. Herbs should be sown in the proportion 20:80 of grass and the herb component in the seed mix adjusted according to seed size and field factors.

Standard seed mix	Simple seed mix
%	%
10 Bird's-foot-trefoil	30 Knapweed/common cat's-ear/hawkbit
10 Cowslip	25 Selfheal
20 Knapweed or common cat's-ear	20 Oxeye daisy
15 Selfheal	25 Yarrow
20 Oxeye daisy	
15 Wild carrot or upright hedge-parsley	
10 Yarrow	

Other suitable herbs could have been listed but the above are readily available in quantity which reduces the cost. More uncommon species, whose seed is expensive, would be better grown in pots and transplanted into a bank. However, advice should be sought from local naturalists to see if the species selected is suitable as an introduction to the area, and whether such conditions as situation and soil type are suitable.

It is recommended that the seeding rate should be 30kg/ha minimum and 40kg/ha maximum.

* The seed mixture has been devised as an all purpose/all soil bank mix. It is not expected that all the species listed will do equally well at each site but efforts have been made to select species likely to produce a sward quickly and to bind the soil well. Specialist seed mixes are available if your local supplier is consulted.

The tables given above were compiled with the help and advice of Mr Geoff Taylor of W W Johnson & Son Ltd, Boston.

Table 5 Trees and shrubs suitable for planting

	Acid	Neutral	Alkaline	No. of associated invertebrate species
<5 metres in height				
Alder		★	★	141
Birch	★		★	334
Blackthorn		★	★	151
Crab apple		★	★	116
Dogwood		★	★	
Field maple		★	★	51
Guelder rose		★	★	
Hawthorn	★	★	★	205
Hazel		★	★	106
Holly	★	★	★	96
Rowan	★	★		58
>5 metres				
Ash		★	★	68
Oak	★	★	★	423
Willows	★	★	★	

Species to be avoided –

Wild cherry — a secondary host to aphids carrying barley mosaic virus so should not be planted close to arable.

Sycamore — seeds prolifically when mature and can invade areas with dense stands of saplings.

Poplar — species tend to produce suckers which can cause problems for access.

Suitable species

Alder — a small tree capable of growing in wet or waterlogged conditions. It has a dense fibrous root system that binds soil well.

Ash — a tall, light demanding tree with an open canopy, often found on river banks. It has a long lateral root system.

Birch — both downy and silver birch can be planted and will form slender graceful trees which are aesthetically pleasing. Downy birch is tolerant of damp sites. Both are light-demanding and should not form part of a mixture of trees for this reason.

Blackthorn — a low dense shrub that is valuable as cover for birds and useful for hedging and faggots.

Dogwood — a low straggling shrub with attractive red stems and colourful autumn leaves. Non-native species should not be planted as they are usually aggressive and will soon dominate the bank.

Field maple — a medium sized tree or hedgerow shrub which is a valuable source of nectar and provides good autumn colour.

Guelder rose — an attractive open shrub with striking white, many flowered heads and good autumn colour.

Hawthorn — a dense medium sized tree or hedgerow shrub useful for faggots. It establishes easily from whips and gives a good stock proof barrier. The white bunches of flowers provide a rich nectar source for insects. Birds benefit from the cover for roosting and nesting whilst the fruit is a valuable food in autumn.

Hazel — a medium to low open shrub that gives an early pollen source and edible nuts in the autumn. It coppices well and the coppice stakes and whips can be used in hedging or sold for pea sticks or for thatching spars.

Holly — this is an evergreen tree or shrub. Male and female flowers are normally on separate trees. The fruit is popular with birds. Its dense shade will kill vegetation beneath so it should not be used where this could be critical. Holly is an excellent hedging shrub and will also coppice well.

Oak — a large open-crowned tree, but slow growing. It is a valuable tree for insects.

Rowan — a medium to tall open tree, light-demanding. The groups of white flowers provide a good nectar source and the fruit is taken by birds.

Willows — they are all fast-growing and tolerant of wet conditions. There are two native tree species and the remainder are shrubs or small trees. Many willow crosses occur and identification can be difficult. Tree species can be pollarded. All can be coppiced. Willow stakes and whips can be used to protect banks from erosion and stabilise embankments. Willows are the foodplant of many moth caterpillars. Many of which fall into the water where fish feed on them.

Tree species — white willow, crack willow.

Shrubs and small trees — osier, goat willow, common sallow, purple willow.

R G Soutar and G F Peterken (1989) gives a regional list of native trees and shrubs. *Arboricultural Journal 13*, 33-43

Herbicides for aquatic and bankside plants

Aquatic and bankside herbicides are one tool in a range of useful management methods. In some cases herbicides may be a more appropriate management method than a mechanical weed control. There are inherent disadvantages and advantages for wildlife whatever method is used. This section gives the range of bankside and aquatic herbicides available to the drainage engineer but also explains some of the pitfalls and advantages of each.

With all methods of maintenance, a key factor in determining what is appropriate is to define the management aim. Basically there are four levels of control when using herbicides –

☐ Complete eradication. Where drainage is the primary aim the need is sometimes for the complete removal of all plant growth. This is only likely where there is a high flood risk. Herbicides which most nearly achieve this aim are the more persistent total herbicides. The effect can last for a whole season.

☐ Seasonal removal. Excessive growth can be removed for part of the year but re-growth occurs within a few weeks. This is the commonest objective and appropriate herbicides can be used both on the banksides and within the drainage channel. By careful timing, fish spawning sites can be conserved early in the season and herbicides used to create open water channels later in the season.

☐ Partial treatment. In some cases it is necessary to remove the vegetation within part of the channel completely, to maintain a drainage function. The benefits of and justification for partial treatment can be varied. It could be that fish spawning sites need to be conserved, or it could be that the total removal of vegetation will cause

de-oxygenation.

☐ Selective treatment. Nuisance or local growths of one type of plant can be removed by periodic spot treatments with appropriate and often less persistent herbicides.

No one herbicide is effective against all plants; hence several have been developed and are available to the river manager. Thirteen years ago, ten herbicide formulations had been approved for use in or alongside water. This compares with the present day approval of thirteen combinations, under the Control of Pesticides Regulations (1986) – see Table 6.

Aquatic plants can only be regarded as weeds when they become a nuisance and interfere with the specific management aims of the watercourses. These are divided, for convenience, into five 'weed groups' – (1) algae, and (2) submerged, (3) floating, (4) emergent and (5) bankside higher plants. The figures in parentheses are referred to in Table 6.

Table 6 shows the spectrum of control achieved from the 12 approved formulations. Some broad spectrum herbicides kill plants on land and in water. Others kill only plants found in water or only those found on land. The broad but sometimes inaccurate division into bankside and aquatic herbicides will be used. Only one formulation (diquat alginate) is designed for use in flowing water above 0.025 metres/second, or 90 metres/hour. Table 7 shows the full list of approved products and the safety interval before irrigation.

Selection of suitable herbicides for aquatic environments

Complete eradication

Terbutryn is the most effective herbicide against both algae and higher plants. It destroys both the root and stem of the higher plant so regrowth must come from sources outside the treated area. Nevertheless it is a tricky herbicide to use. Its efficiency seems to be dependent on water temperatures exceeding 16°C. Whilst it is extremely effective at controlling algae it cannot be used to control this group of plants without killing off higher plants.

A level of 0.1 mg l^{-1} is recommended to kill algae and 0.05 mg l^{-1} for higher plants but many plants are still killed at 0.01 mg l^{-1}. Treatment of a quarter of a lake sprayed at 0.05 mg l^{-1} could effectively kill most higher plants through diffusion and mixing. Unlike some herbicides, terbutryn cannot be used for spot treatment as it readily diffuses into untreated areas. The overall effective and final concentration would be 0.0125 mg l^{-1}.

The herbicide is for the reasons given above, phyto-toxic for many months against the regrowth of higher plants but it is less persistent against the control of algae. Post-treatment algal problems could occur. Such a herbicide should thus be used with extra caution and never in a site of known botanical interest.

Seasonal removal

Diquat is a quick-acting contact herbicide so it tends to stay where applied. It is a total herbicide of low persistence, killing a wide spectrum of submerged and emergent aquatic plants. The herbicide is absorbed through leaf and stem and the shoot may die before the roots are killed. Some regrowth of the original plant is possible.

Diquat is also formulated with an alginate; as such it is suitable for use in flowing water since the herbicide sticks to plants. There are occasions when the formulation is only partially effective. Diquat is known to be inactivated when the organic content of the water is high, being readily absorbed onto organic particles; it also breaks down rapidly in UV light. Too much or too little calcium and an excess of sodium in the water can also impair its efficiency.

Partial treatment

Total herbicides such as dichlobenil and dichlobenil GSR are broad spectrum herbicides. In part their persistence in water is due to the formulation. GSR stands for granule slow release. Both are applied in granular form which is made from calcium and/or fuller's earth. The granule dissolves slowly around a root mat and the herbicide is translocated through the root system to the stem.

Both types of granule dissolve slowly and are phytotoxic for around 21 days and 28-40 days respectively. Some herbicide will diffuse away from the site of treatment but dilution renders it non-phytotoxic so it can be used for the partial treatment of a water body. Partial herbicide control can be expected along the inner edge of the diffusion zone so it cannot be used to spot-treat plants.

Selective treatment

Diquat can be used for the selective spot-treatment of nuisance plants, and has been used by wildlife trusts and the Nature Conservancy Council. Diquat alginate can be used with greater accuracy and can even spot-treat small areas in flowing water.

Margins and wetland

Dalapon, 2,4-D amine, and glyphosate control both bankside species and some aquatic species. They cannot control submerged species but will control some floating and emergent species provided the leaf surface is dry.

Dalapon is very successful in dominant stands of common reed. It can be used to clear large or small areas but it will kill other narrow-leaved emergent wetland plants if the reeds are not totally dominant. It has been used with great success by the Royal Society for the Protection of Birds creating open water areas within reed-beds; the decay of the rhizomes creates shallow open-water lagoons.

2,4-D amine and the one formulation of 2,4-D amine/chlorpropham/maleic hydrazide have been used to control water lilies. In water, both herbicides seem to control species with floating leaves, whilst on land they kill a wide range of wetland broad-leaved plants – see Table 6.

Selection of herbicides for banksides

Asulam is the only selective bankside herbicide being most used for dock and bracken control. Fosamine ammonium, 2,4-D amine, 2,4-D amine/ Chlorpropham/Maleic hydrazide tend to control specific groups of plants – see Table 6. A wide number of species are found in each of these 'weed groups' and so they are selective to a particular group rather than to a species.

Glyphosate is a total broad spectrum bankside and emergent herbicide. It is very useful for eradicating problem weeds. It does not spread on application and has been used on a local county council nature reserve to spot-treat invading sea club-rush. This chemical is almost too effective where the soil has a high organic component. In these situations it stays active for up to a year. Its use should be limited since it can create bare earth after widescale spraying on organically rich banksides; this can easily result in bankside erosion.

Ecological benefits and problems associated with herbicide use

There is a standard procedure to follow before using any aquatic herbicide. These are considered in detail in the *Guidelines on the use of herbicides on weeds in or near watercourses and lakes.* (MAFF 1985). For example, any user is bound by the laws on pollution and must obtain permission from the appropriate authority and be a certificated user in accordance with the legislation. Equally they must take due account of the nature conservation interest within Sites of Special Scientific Interest and consult the Nature Conservancy Council.

In addition to the MAFF guidelines, the user must fully consider the ecological consequences of inappropriate choices of herbicides, or their use when mechanical methods would be more suitable.

All herbicides in this chapter have passed rigorous tests and are approved by the Control of Pesticide Regulations (1986) making them safe for use in waters containing fish and other animal life.

However, many herbicides directly kill some invertebrates although the impact in general will be very small. Some species of snails, for example, are killed using diquat, even at the recommended dose. Some invertebrates may be stressed by a herbicide. An example is a white form of water-boatman found in a pond treated with dichlobenil GSR. If fish are killed directly by a herbicide then the treatment level has been far too high. However the safety margin is small for one herbicide, dichlobenil GSR. For this reason a method of partial treatment has been developed.

A major pitfall when using aquatic or bankside herbicides is that they can be used to eradicate large areas of vegetation. This gross treatment can cause an ecological backlash, changing the species composition to one which can only be treated by other herbicides such as terbutryn. Consequently the management options open to the engineer are reduced as algae may dominate in the space of a few seasons. Algae cannot be removed satisfactorily by mechanical methods and so the system often becomes herbicide-dependent.

Aquatic herbicides controlling submerged vegetation are generally applied in the spring when plant growth is low. The aquatic fauna may be dependent on the increased plant production for its cycle of growth and reproduction. Food production can be suddenly cut off and the ability of an animal to survive may depend on migration. Some invertebrate species are plant-specific and where herbicides have been used to destroy specific plants, the animals have also been affected.

Plants also provide refuges from predation, for both fish and invertebrates. Fish spawning sites should not be sprayed if a healthy fishery is to be maintained. Mechanical methods would probably have the same effect, if used during early spring, but they need not be tied to this season.

Oxygen depletion can be a major problem following a herbicide application.

In slow-flowing or stagnant water the degree of oxygen depletion following herbicide treatment depends on the amount of plants prior to treatment. Bacteria break down any dying plant tissue following herbicides application and this process demands oxygen. If the amount of dying vegetation is high, the drop in oxygen can cause fish deaths.

To reduce the severity of a sudden oxygen loss, partial treatment can be carried out by spraying a third or a quarter of the total area at any one time. An interval of two to three weeks is recommended between treatments if the management aim is one of complete eradication.

Herbicides can destroy large areas of wildlife habitats because of the speed and ease with which they can be applied. It is probable that an efficient operator using a mowing bucket will remove more plants and animals than herbicides in a similar ditch. However mowing buckets are relatively slow in comparison with applications of herbicides. Areas which may take one season to clear could be treated in a matter of days with a herbicide. The bucket may be killing both plant and animal species directly by removal, but the rate of habitat destruction can be slow. Herbicides can bring about a massive and rapid change in habitat.

The ease of application of herbicides is one of their advantages. Any herbicide that is used intensively and extensively can be capable of destroying or changing the aquatic flora of whole catchment areas. Re-colonisation by the original plant and animal life from an unsprayed area into the core of the sprayed area could take

years even after only one herbicide application. Herbicides have the potential to destroy balanced communities resulting in single-species dominance or invasion of non-susceptible species such as algae.

As there are no suitable mechanical methods for removing algae, the great danger is that a system may become herbicide-dependent. The engineer who uses herbicides in this way gains very little and could be faced with greater expense to keep the channel clear.

Herbicides should be looked on as one effective tool in an integrated approach to channel management. Most plants are a favoured habitat for many invertebrates, whereas algae are not. Management programmes which aim to maintain and promote fisheries, nature conservation or amenity should consider only those herbicides which partially or spot-treat the vegetation. The more total an aquatic herbicide, the more it should be used with caution, with strict adherence to the MAFF *Guidelines on the use of herbicides in or near water.*

Grass carp

Grass carp are exotic herbivorous alien fish originating from China. They are able to control the excessive growth of certain species of aquatic plants but like most animals they have certain food preferences and these change with age.

In other parts of Europe, including eastern Russia, these fish have been released on a wide scale into watercourses where plants are a problem. In such areas it is assumed that they are a help in water-weed control although there is no means of measuring their effectiveness as there are few untreated channels. In many the stocking density would be so low as to make them ineffective as a controlling agent. Large scale and generally uncontrolled introductions are an uneconomic way of using grass carp. Plant growth can only be controlled effectively at the correct density of fish. Too few fish and their effect is hardly noticeable (which may be the case in many eastern European countries), too many fish and the watercourses will be a desert. Starvation causes the fish to eat even the most unpalatable species, and fish will even leap out and graze emergent plants. Correct stocking densities of grass carp can only be maintained if the fish are introduced into enclosed waters. In these situations they can be an effective agent against excessive weed growth. Their introduction could beneficially affect the ecology of an excessively weeded system. Conversely, where grass carp are introduced into a reasonably balanced and healthy watercourse, the ecology could be adversely affected and natural fish populations could suffer.

Site introduction

The introduction of grass carp into any enclosed lake, pond or drainage channel has to be approved by the river authority under Section 30 of the Salmon and Freshwater Fisheries Act 1975, which must sanction any movements of fish in England and Wales. Their introduction also has to be approved under the Wildlife and Countryside Act 1981 and a licence must be obtained from the Ministry of Agriculture, Fisheries and Food (MAFF). The Fisheries Officer of the National Rivers Authority will give advice on where to obtain the fish and will probably inspect the proposed site. The site must be secure with no likelihood of the fish getting dispersed into other waters. So any site which floods regularly will not be approved.

Food preferences

Grass carp will not normally eat all species of water plants. They prefer some species to others but as they grow larger their selection widens.

Eaten readily –
    Duckweeds
    Stoneworts
    Canadian pondweed
    Starworts
    Small-leaved pondweeds

Eaten less readily –
    Hornwort
    Milfoils
    Water moss
    Mare's-tail
    Water buttercup
    Larger-leaved and floating
      pondweeds

Plants usually avoided include water-lilies and emergent species (for example, reeds and sedges).
Grass carp will eat some filamentous algae such as *Enteromorpha* and *Cladophora, Spirogyra* and *Vaucheria* are less attractive to the fish.

Water temperatures

Grass carp are a sub-tropical species and, despite some acclimatisation are only stimulated into heavy grazing when water temperatures exceed 16°C.
A warm spring will ensure that the fish are active enough to control the growth of plants. Cold springs are more normal, however, and the plants will reach a peak of growth before the water is warm enough for the fish to become really active. True weed control may be delayed until late summer unless some supplementary management, such as cutting, takes place. Spring-fed water maintains a moderate all-year-round temperature, generally below 16°C, and such waters are not really suitable for grass carp.

Stocking density

Fish about 20 centimetres long and 100 grams in weight should be introduced into an enclosed site in late spring or early summer.
Being fairly large they will be less susceptible to predation and by the first winter will have grown enough to survive what is a six month period of low temperature. In the following year the stocking density should be between 200 kilograms and 300 kilograms per hectare. Advice can be obtained from the National Rivers Authority on the number of 100 gram fish needed to reach this desired stocking rate.

After one or two seasons the fish will have gained more weight and the stocking rate may well exceed these recommendations. Some may have to be moved elsewhere although inevitably some will have succumbed through cold or predation. The fish on average live for about seven to nine years but they can reach an age of 16 years or so.

Plants ungrazed by grass carp could be removed by cutting or herbicide treatments but many could be left, such as the water lilies and emergent plants, since the complete elimination of plants is usually undesirable and unnecessary.

The effects on other fish

Grass carp should not breed in this country since the eggs are adapted to developing in warm, sub-tropical, well-oxygenated rivers where water temperatures exceed 20°C. Research by MAFF and others has shown that grass carp have little adverse effect and possibly even some beneficial effect on indigenous fish species; although heavy grazing through over-stocking could affect their spawning sites. However, any form of chemical or mechanical weed removal could have the same effect but such management could be scheduled outside the spawning season. No such control is available with grass carp. Conversely, in polluted waters the control of algae by grass carp can increase floral diversity, which might enhance invertebrate and fish populations.

Grass carp should be looked on as one more tool in the management of aquatic plants. There are many disadvantages as well as advantages. The Welland and Deeping IDB have conducted trials on a working watercourse since 1983. Results show that the degree of clearance can be controlled by the stocking density and it is possible to have partial clearance, where the grazing patterns tend to create patches of open water much liked by fishermen and conservationists.

Table 6 The choice of herbicide formulations and their spectra of weed control

'Weed groups'	Terbutryn	Dichlobenil	Dichlobenil GSR	Dichlobenil. dalapon	Diquat/diquat alginate	Dalapon	Glyphosate	Maleic hydrazide	2,4-D amine	2,4-D amine Chlorpropham Maleic hydrazide	Asulam	Fosamine ammonium
(1) Algae	K				MR							
(2) Submerged plants	K	K	K	K	K							
(3) Free-floating plants (small leaf area)	K				K							
(3) Floating-leaved plants (large leaf area)		K	K	K			K		MR	MR		
(4) Reeds				K		K	MR					
(4) Sedges				MR		MR	K					
(5) Grasses and rushes							K	K		K		
(5) Broad-leaved weeds							K	K	K	K		
(5) Docks							K				K	
(5) Trees and shrubs												K

Figures in parentheses refer to 'weed group'
K = Kill; MR = Moderately resistant

Where a choice of chemical exists select the one affecting the least number of non-target groups.

NB. Paraquat is not approved for use in water even though it kills a similar spectrum of plants.

Table 7 List of approved products for use as herbicides on weeds in or near watercourses and lakes

Chemical	Safety interval before irrigation	Approved products	MAFF No.	For control of ...
Asulam	nil	Asulox	00122	Bracken and docks on banks beside water
Chlorthiamid	4 weeks	Prefix (discontinued)	01630	Some floating and submerged weeds
2,4-D amine	3 weeks	Atlas 2,4-D Chipman 2,4-D Dormone Mascot Economy Selective (withdrawn) Mega D Fernimine	03052 00498 00751 03008 01319 00863	Floating and emergent water weeds and many broad leaf weeds on banks of waterway or ditch
2,4-D amine Chlorpropham + maleic hydrazide	3 weeks	Vondrax	02319	Weeds on banks of watercourses
Dalapon	5 weeks	Atlas Herbon Dalapon B H Dalapon Dowpon M SDS Dalapon	03100 03047 03302 02630	Control of reeds and similar emergent weeds
Dichlobenil	2 weeks	Casoron G (ICI) Casoran G (Syn-Chemicals) Casoran GSR Prefix D	00448 00449 00451 01631	Floating and submerged weeds
Dichlobenil + Dalapon	non stated	Fydulan	00958	Weed and reed control near water
Diquat/ Diquat alginate	10 days	Reglone Midstream	01713 01348	Floating and submerged weeds and algae Submerged weeds in still or moving water
Fosamine ammonium	nil	Krenite	01165	Deciduous trees and shrubs on banks beside water
Glyphosate	nil	Roundup (Monsanto) Roundup (FBC Ltd) Roundup Pro Sonic Spaser Herbicide New Formulation	01828 03620 04146 03376 03436	Emergent and floating weeds including reeds and water-lillies
Maleic hydrazide	3 weeks	Bos MH Bos MH 180 Lowcut Regulox K Vondalhyde K	03589 04327 03159 01716 03064	Weeds and grass on river banks
Terbutryn	7 days	Clarosan Clarosan IFG	00520 03859	Floating and submerged weeds and algae

Reproduced with permission, by Terry Tooby of MAFF

This chapter is not only concerned with the loss of wet grassland and the effect this is having on the breeding success of a group of wading birds. It also serves to emphasise the opportunities which exist to raise the water levels and reverse some of the trends. Where possible the elevation of retained water levels on both a permanent and temporary basis should be considered as part of the broader water management programme.

Traditional forms of agriculture in the lowlands have created an attractive landscape and a habitat for a range of breeding birds. Low intensity farming of poorly drained grasslands with summer grazing and a single cut for hay permits a group of wading birds to breed successfully. These include lapwing, redshank, snipe and occasionally black-tailed godwit and ruff. For these birds to breed successfully and to maintain a healthy population in the UK, close co-operation is required between conservationists, farmers and drainage authorities.

Post-war policy and Government encouragement of the intensification of agriculture has resulted in the decline in all the breeding waders of lowland wet grasslands. With the exception of the lapwing, lowland breeding waders are now confined to a very small number of sites in England. Appropriate management of water level and farming practices on these sites is necessary to maintain and enhance the breeding populations. The sympathetic management of additional sites would allow numbers to expand to a level where the long-term future of breeding populations is assured.

The improvement in drainage and the intensification of agriculture act together to produce a set of conditions which prevent wading birds feeding and breeding successfully. Installations and improvement of land drainage lowers the water table and can remove temporary pools. This reduces available feeding opportunities for wading birds. The soil dries out faster in the spring and allows grazing livestock to be turned out earlier in the year. This results in a greater proportion of eggs being trampled by livestock. Further intensification of production systems include re-seeding of the pasture and heavier applications of fertilizer. These are accompanied by heavier stocking densities which lead to greater egg and chick losses by trampling. Cutting of the sward for silage results in total loss of eggs and chicks. The final stage in intensification, through improvement in drainage, is conversion of the land to an arable production system with the loss of virtually all breeding waders. Fortunately, it appears that in some cases the effect upon breeding waders of improved drainage is reversible. Land owned by conservation bodies in the Somerset Levels and Nene Washes have supported high densities of breeding waders only a few years after intensive agricultural production ceased and drainage standards were relaxed. Such rapid recolonisation by waders can only be expected where successful breeding populations exist close by.

The value of traditionally farmed landscapes and the wildlife that they support has been acknowledged by the Government with the creation of Environmentally Sensitive Areas (ESA). Within these designated areas payment is available to farmers who follow prescriptions which maintain the landscape and nature conservation value of their land. In a typical ESA containing wet grassland there are several 'tiers' of payment depending upon the measures taken by the farmer. The greatest payment per hectare may be made available to the farmer who manages his grassland in a manner which can encourage breeding waders. To receive this high rate of payment it is necessary for the farmer to maintain a high water level in the ditches surrounding the fields concerned. Close co-operation between the farmer and the drainage authority is vital if the farmer is to be able to maintain a high water level in the ditches and is to receive the higher tier ESA payments. The specific prescription to receive payments varies between ESAs and the staff of the drainage authority in each area should discuss with the relevant

MAFF ESA project officer how their activities can be conducted in a manner which is sympathetic to the aims of the ESA.

For waders to breed successfully on grassland, food supply, water levels, soil and vegetation structure have to be suitable. These factors are inter-related and can be influenced by the activities of a drainage authority. The five species of wader breeding on wet grassland have slightly different needs and if measures are to be taken to encourage them, consideration should be given to the relative status of the species in the area before deciding on a course of action. This is best carried out in consultation with local and national conservation bodies who will be able to advise on which of the five waders are most in need of protective measures in the area.

Scientific research carried out in the UK by the conservation bodies has identified those factors which are required for four out of the five waders of wet grassland to breed successfully. The ruff is now so scarce that information is lacking upon its requirements from studies in the UK. However, work in the Netherlands has shown that the ruff is the most sensitive to agricultural improvement. For the remaining four species a summary is given below but, if specific management measures are proposed, relevant conservation bodies should be contacted for further advice.

Redshank

Adult redshanks spend much of their time feeding at the edges of pools and ditches, pecking at aquatic invertebrates and small insects on vegetation and water surface. Some prey may be taken by probing in mud or moist soil. Although adults may fly over a kilometre to feed, redshank nests are most abundant in fields with pools. A grass sward with tussocks produced by cattle grazing is required since the tussocks provide nest sites. Redshank chicks are moved by the adults, soon after hatching from the nest site, to the edges of pools and ditches.

Lapwing

Lapwings locate their food by eye, rather than by probing and then run to peck it from the surface of the soil and vegetation. They favour bare ground and short vegetation for feeding with the highest nesting densities occurring where the grass sward is less than 15 centimetres in height in mid-May. During incubation adult lapwings tend to feed within 300 metres of the nest. The chicks, on hatching, are moved to the edge of pools or to short grassland where they feed in a similar way to their parents.

Snipe

Snipe feed by probing mud and soft soil for earthworms and insect larvae. Peat soils provide better feeding conditions than silt or clay derived soils. They will feed among taller vegetation than other waders. During incubation of the eggs, the female snipe feeds within 70 metres of the nest if feeding conditions are suitable. Flying longer distances to find feeding sites may expose them and the nest to predators. Snipe chicks, unlike most other waders, are fed at first by their parents and move only slowly away from the nest site. As a consequence suitable feeding conditions of a soft soil are required close to the nest site. A grass sward with tussocks produced by cattle grazing is required since the tussocks provide nest sites.

Black-tailed godwit

Black-tailed godwits probe in mud and soil for earthworms and insect larvae and also wade in shallow pools taking mud dwelling invertebrates. During the incubation of the eggs the male godwit will feed close to the nest in order to be able to ward off potential predators of the eggs such as crows. The chicks feed by picking insects from vegetation but also take insect larvae from the soil and shallow pools. The black-tailed godwit prefers to nest in short vegetation and highest densities occur where the grass sward is less than 15 centimetres high in mid-May.

In order to enhance the populations of waders in the UK it is necessary both to manage the land appropriately and to maintain suitable water levels. The water table needs to be held at around 20 centimetres below the soil surface throughout the breeding season of March to August. If the water table is held below this level the soil dries out and becomes too hard for waders to probe for worms and insect larvae. If it is held at a higher level, anaerobic conditions can develop in the soil which reduces the food supply, especially earthworms, for waders. The field drainage system of sub-surface pipes, if present, can be used to maintain damp conditions within the field. If the level of the water in the ditch is held above the field outfall then water will move through the pipes to the centre of the field. This occurs considerably more rapidly than does horizontal movement of water from the ditch through the soil. In larger fields this may be the only way to achieve a suitable water table within the field. This form of controlled irrigation can only be achieved by the relevant drainage authorities holding back and releasing water where appropriate.

If depressions are present in the fields and water tables are held sufficiently high, shallow pools can be maintained during the breeding season which will benefit redshank, lapwing and black-tailed godwit. Care should be taken to avoid spring and summer flooding of fields used for nesting which will lead to the loss of eggs and small chicks. This can be prevented through appropriate water management via pumps and sluices. Low bunds parallel to, but set back from, the river can limit the extent of the flooding, protecting some areas containing wader nests.

Where the IDB is responsible for the management of the land in flood storage areas, as well as the drainage channels, then measures can be taken in addition to those above. Shallow depressions can be created which, with a high water table, will produce pools and damp areas in the field throughout the breeding season. The grass should be grazed rather than cut but stock should not be put out into the field until mid-June to prevent the trampling of eggs and small chicks. It has been found that a grazing intensity of around 250-300 cow-days per hectare in the summer produces a sward the following spring most suitable for breeding waders.

Consideration should be given to the appropriate elevation of water levels on a field by field or isolated catchment basis, using sluice boards. See Option 14.

The future

Agricultural overproduction is being tackled through various mechanisms, including farm diversification, extensification, set-aside and Environmentally Sensitive Areas. It is estimated that some three to five million hectares will be taken out of production or be at a lower level of production by the end of the century. The present options for wildlife in and alongside the drainage channel are constrained by a design which has been economical of land take. If land is set aside by the drainage channel then the options for wildlife are greatly increased.

Some of the management ideas in this manual require some extra land, mainly as marginal strips, However, set-aside allows expanded margins from 15 metres wide to whole fields and even whole farms to be taken out of production. The constraint of the linear habitat could be removed by expanding some of the ideas in this manual using wide field margins or whole fields set aside to restore drained marshes and fens. Along the coast, set-aside land could be used to re-create grazing marsh.

The gradual rise in sea level also presents many wildlife opportunities, allowing marginal agricultural land to revert to saltmarsh or other habitats. The cost of maintaining an expensive sea-wall to protect unwanted agricultural land could well be prohibitive. A valuable wildlife habitat could be restored and the salt marsh would act as a soft form of coastal defence, absorbing wave energy before the waves hit the 'new' sea-wall, now placed further back. Coastal defence lines need not be constructed from new. Former sea-walls, now inland, could be repaired and used as a cheaper option for coastal defence. A rise in sea level could also see the need for wider channels inland, or an increased bank height. One option would be to construct new washland areas or re-instate former washlands.

Glossary of terms

animal   Every living thing that is not a plant is an animal. The term covers, for example, insects, spiders, worms, mammals, birds.

amphibians   A term to cover animals that spend part of their life in water, for example, toads, frogs and newts.

aquatic plants   A term given to plants that grow entirely covered by water, like water-milfoil, or at the surface, such as yellow water-lily. Some plants have both aquatic and emergent forms.

berm   A shelf at the base of a bank that is at the level of normal flow and gives extra channel width in high flows. It is normally planted with emergents and the channel is kept free of plants for drainage purposes.

braided channel   A situation where water in a channel splits around a series of obstructions such as shoals, then recombines only to split again.

carr   Wet woodland composed of trees such as willow and alder.

channel   The portion of a watercourse actually carrying water.

community (of plants and/or animals)   In nature certain plants and animals are often to be found together. They may be interdependent and the association is called a community.

coppicing   Traditional management of trees and shrubs for wood production by cutting stems close to the base with a slanting cut to shed water and removing the regrowth periodically.

diversity   A term used to indicate that there are or could be many kinds of plants or animals present given the right conditions. It relates not only to the number of species present but also to their abundance.

dry matter production   The quantity of plant material left after drying.

emergent plants   Those plants that grow in water but have leaf structures that emerge above the surface, for example, bulrush.

fringe   A term used to describe plants growing along the boundary of the water and the bank.

habitat   Place with a particular kind of environment inhabited by organisms, for example, grassland or water.

higher plants   All plants excluding fungi, mosses, lichens and algae.

hydrology   The study of water and its dynamics.

invertebrates   Animals without a backbone, for example, insects, worms, spiders.

litter   Dead plant and material left when banks are cut or which collects where vegetation is not cut at all.

macrophytes   Another term for the 'higher plants'.

margins   A term used to describe the junction of the water and the bank.

micro-habitats   Describes the conditions that individual or small groups of individual plants or animals live in.

monocultures   Vegetation completely dominated by one type of plant.

mosaic of plants   Describes plants growing in an intimate mixture rather than as monocultures.

pH   A scale of 14 points indicating the degree of acidity or alkalinity of water with 7 as neutral.

plant productivity   Density of growth or quantity yielded.

pollarding   Method of managing trees, particularly willows, by cutting the stem at head height or higher and letting it sprout. Recutting the new branches (pollards) takes place periodically.

propagules (plant)   Portions of aquatic plants that break off and take root elsewhere in a channel.

recolonisation   The spread of plants back into a gap left by drainage works.

reptiles   Animals such as snakes and lizards.

rhizomes   Underground stems which produce shoots at a distance from the parent plant.

rosette   Plant leaves growing flat and close to the ground.

rugosity   Degree of resistance to water flow caused by different materials.

stoloniferous   Plant stems that extend and form plants above the ground (for example, strawberry plants).

toe   The base of a bank.

Further reading

** *Aquatic Plants: A guide to recognition.* David Spencer-Jones and Max Wade. ICI, 1986. Available from ICI Professional products, Woolmead Walk, Farnham, Surrey, 0252 724525.

* *British Wild Flowers for Habitat Creation and Landscaping.* Emorsgate Seeds, Terrington Court, Terrington St Clement, King's Lynn, Norfolk.

** *Butterflies of the British Isles.* J A Thomas. Hamlyn, 1986.

Changing River Landscapes. Countryside Commission CCP 238, 1987.

Code of Guidance for Sites of Special Scientific Interest. Department of the Environment, Ministry of Agriculture, Fisheries and Food, Scottish Office, Welsh Office. HMSO. 1986.

** *Collins Field Guide to Freshwater Life.* R Fitter and R Manuel. Collins, 1986.

Conservation and Land Drainage Guidelines. Water Space. Amenity Commission. 1980.

Conservation guidelines for Drainage Authorities. Ministry of Agriculture, Fisheries and Food. 1988.

Guidelines for the use of herbicides on weeds in or near watercourses and lakes. Ministry of Agriculture, Fisheries and Food. 1985.

Nature conservation and river engineering. Nature Conservancy Council. C Newbold, J Purseglove, and N T H Holmes. 1983.

Protecting Britain's Wildlife. DoE. 1988.

Rivers and Wildlife Handbook : A guide to practices which further the conservation of wildlife on rivers. RSPB. G Lewis, and G Williams. 1984.

The History and Ecology of the Norfolk Broads. Packard Publishing, Chichester, M George (To be published later).

The Water Industry in the Countryside. Countryside Commission CCP 239, 1988.

** *The Wildflower Key.* Francis Rose. Frederick Warne, 1981.

Wetland and riparian plants in Great Britain. Nature Conservancy Council. M Palmer, and C Newbold, 1983.

* *Wild Flower Guide.* Johnsons Seeds, London Road, Boston, Lincs.

** Field guides
* Inexpensive booklets with advice on plants, sowing and maintenance.

Land drainage is generally understood to include the alleviation or prevention of flooding of urban and agricultural land, whether by freshwater or saltwater, including the improvement and maintenance of natural watercourses, and the construction and maintenance of man-made channels and structures used for these purposes. It also includes water level management and the provision of flood warning systems.

In land drainage there are no absolute standards of protection. The degree of protection attainable is dependent on the cost of the works against the benefits achieved. It follows that the protection of urban areas provides greater benefits than that of rural areas and hence schemes providing a higher standard of protection can be funded. Present arrangements require that all schemes meet cost/benefit criteria established by MAFF which provides grants towards such works.

Legislation dealing with land drainage has existed in England and Wales for at least 500 years. The statutes and common law have evolved out of the need to resolve practical problems and were extremely complex prior to the important Land Drainage Act of 1930, which greatly clarified and consolidated the situation. A further consolidation was effected by the Act of 1976, which incorporated most of the previous statutes and included the earlier Acts of 1930 and 1961 and repealed 25 earlier Acts in whole or part, including parts of the Water Act of 1973.

Common law precedents and statutory provisions have established the general principles which govern the present arrangements which can be summarised as follows.

Individual owners are responsible for the drainage of their own land and for dealing with and accepting the natural catchment flows from adjoining land. They must not permit an obstruction to the natural flow.

Powers given to public authorities are in general permissive, thereby recognising the rights and obligations of riparian owners and other individuals and giving such authorities a degree of choice in terms of public expenditure priorities.

Permissive powers are available to a local authority, or an IDB where one exists, to enable it to carry out flood prevention work on all watercourses which are not main rivers. Such work may therefore be funded from the rates within the local area concerned.

Along with MAFF's grant aid and other direct contributions the underlying principle is that, except for main rivers, the decision to give priority to funding and to carry out work on a particular watercourse rests with the internal drainage board, the local authority, or the riparian owner.

In the case of designated main rivers, which generally carry water from the uplands through to the sea, certain powers and duties rest with the National Rivers Authority (NRA) which draws its funds from the whole catchment. Apart from the mandatory duty of general supervision, the statutory provisions in connection with main rivers confer discretionary powers of control and permissive powers to do work including maintenance and improvement.

Under the Water Acts of 1973 and 1989, drainage authorities have been given special duties to further conservation, because of the potential damage to wildlife and habitats that can be caused by drainage operations. These are set out in an illustrated booklet *Conservation Guidelines for Drainage Authorities* published by MAFF, DoE and the Welsh Office in 1988.

The guidelines emphasise the need to consult well in advance with the NCC and other relevant conservation bodies when drawing up maintenance programmes or planning any capital works, including changes in water level management.

Where the land is notified as a Site of Special Scientific Interest (SSSI), drainage authorities may have a direct interest as an owner or occupier. In these cases they are provided with a list of potentially damaging operations by the NCC and required to give 4 months' notice of their intention to carry any of them out. They are also required to consult the NCC before carrying out works, operations or activities likely to damage any SSSI. This includes drainage operations elsewhere in a catchment, which could affect water tables in the SSSI. Some sites may also be designated under the Ramsar Convention on Wetlands of International Importance and the EC Directive on Conservation of Wild Birds. Both of these impose certain obligations on the Government, which are explained in DoE Circular 2787.

In addition, the NRA must consult the NCC before authorising any works likely to damage an SSSI; this will involve land-drainage consents and abstraction licences. The NRA also has a duty to promote the conservation of flora and fauna which are dependent on an aquatic environment.

In designing schemes and considering the necessity of any works, drainage authorities are required to take account of any effect they may have on wildlife and natural features. Land Drainage Improvement Works (Assessment of Environmental Effects) Regulations, were issued in July 1988. These require drainage authorities to consider whether an environmental assessment is required before undertaking any improvement works (as defined in the Land Drainage Act 1976.) This involves advertising the proposals and their intention; and procedures for representations by conservation bodies and other interests.

Index

trees 7 19 34 47 49-50 64 68-72 74-77
  alder 8 50 64 69 80
  ash 64 69 74
  fruit trees 62
  hawthorn 50
  oak 69
  willow 68-69 80

Vale of Trent 7

Wales 20-21 101
washland 7 10 16 19 24 78 97
water
  depth 14-17 19-20 24 34 45
  depth in relation to wildlife interest
  17-18 23 46 48
  enrichment 20 25 35 58
  manipulating levels 9 19 24 40 94-96
  open water 24 91
  pH 11 25
  quality and wildlife interest 20 23 25 35
  saline 11 17 25
  seepage 80
  stability of levels for wildlife
  11 20 23 25 34 40
  table 11 20 25 40 94 96
wave erosion 19
weir 39 61 64
Welland and Deeping IDB 25 91
West Sedgemoor 10-11
wet fences 9 17 19 21 40
wetland
  ancient 7 13 21
Whittlesey Mere 11
wildlife
  benefited by continuity 27
  benefited by physical diversity 24
  opportunities in management for 21-22
  24 96
Wildlife and Countryside Act 1981 15-16
90
Woodwalton Fen 7